Teacher Annotated Edition

Science Notebook

Glencoe Science

CHEMISTRY
MATTER AND CHANGE

Consultant
Douglas Fisher, PhD

 Glencoe

New York, New York   Columbus, Ohio   Chicago, Illinois   Woodland Hills, California

About the Consultant

Douglas Fisher, PhD, is a Professor in the Department of Teacher Education at San Diego State University. He is the recipient of an International Reading Association Celebrate Literacy Award as well as a Christa McAuliffe award for Excellence in Teacher Education. He has published numerous articles on reading and literacy, differentiated instruction, and curriculum design as well as books, such as *Improving Adolescent Literacy: Strategies at Work* and *Responsive Curriculum Design in Secondary Schools: Meeting the Diverse Needs of Students*. He has taught a variety of courses in SDSU's teacher credentialing program as well as graduate-level courses on English language development and literacy. He also has taught classes in English, writing, and literacy development to secondary school students.

The McGraw·Hill Companies

 Glencoe

Send all inquiries to:
Glencoe/McGraw-Hill
8787 Orion Place
Columbus, OH 43240-4027

ISBN: 978-0-07-878754-6
MHID: 0-07-878754-8

Printed in the United States of America.

1 2 3 4 5 6 7 8 9 10 047 11 10 09 08 07

Table of Contents

Table of Contents

Dear Science Teacher,

As you begin a new school year, one of the biggest challenges you will probably encounter is getting students to read their textbooks. Informational text can overwhelm students, leaving them less likely to read and more likely to become apathetic about learning. I believe that this Science Notebook will help students use their textbooks more effectively as they learn about Chemistry.

Note-Taking and Student Success

There is considerable research evidence that addresses how students understand difficult concepts and content in school. Glencoe/McGraw-Hill has developed the *Science Notebook* for science students based upon that research. Evidence indicates that students need to know how to take notes, use graphic organizers, learn vocabulary, and develop their thinking skills by writing in order to achieve academic success.

The ability to take and organize notes predicts how well students will do in school. Peverly, Brobst, Graham, and Shaw (2003) showed that when students use background knowledge and take notes, they are likely to perform well on tests. Pauk (1974) observed that note-taking was a critical skill for college success. Notes serve as an external storage function (meaning on the paper) that builds comprehension and content understanding (Ganske, 1981). This *Science Notebook* is a tool that students can use to achieve this goal. I would like to share some of the features of this *Science Notebook* with you before you begin teaching.

The Cornell Note-Taking System

First, you will notice that the pages in the *Science Notebook* are arranged in two columns, which will help students organize their thinking. This two-column design is based on the **Cornell Note-Taking System**, developed at Cornell University. Faber, Morris, and Lieberman (2000) found that the Cornell Note-Taking System improves comprehension and increases test scores.

The column on the left side of the page highlights the main ideas and vocabulary of the lesson. This column will help students find information and locate the references in their textbooks quickly. Students can also use this column to sketch drawings that help them visually remember the lesson's information. In the column on the right side of the page, students will write detailed notes about the main ideas and vocabulary. The notes they take in this column will help them focus on the important information in the lesson. As students become more comfortable using the Cornell Note-Taking System, they will see that it is an important tool that helps them organize information.

The Importance of Graphic Organizers

Second, there are many graphic organizers in this *Science Notebook*. Graphic organizers allow students to see the lesson's important information in a visual format. In addition, graphic organizers help students summarize information and remember the content. I hope that you will encourage students to use the graphic organizers because they will help them understand what they are reading.

Research-Based Vocabulary Development

Third, you will notice that vocabulary is introduced and practiced throughout the *Science Notebook*. When students know the meaning of the words used to discuss information, they are able to understand that information better. Also, students are more likely to be successful in school when they have vocabulary knowledge. When researchers study successful students, they find that as students acquire vocabulary knowledge, their ability to learn improves (Martino and Hoffman, 2002). The *Science Notebook* focuses on learning words that are very specific to understanding the content of the textbook. The *Science Notebook* also highlights general academic words that students need to know so that they can understand any textbook. These vocabulary words are based on the Academic Word List (AWL) developed by Averil Coxhead. The AWL includes the most common 570 words found in academic texts, excluding the 2,000 general English words such as *the*, *in*, and *that*. Research indicates that students who master the words on Coxhead's list score significantly higher on standardized tests.

Writing Prompts and Note-Taking

Finally, there are a number of writing exercises included in this *Science Notebook*. Writing is a useful tool that helps students understand the information that is being presented. Writing helps them to assess what they have learned. You will see that many of the writing exercises require students to practice the skills of good readers. Good readers *make connections* between their lives and the text and *predict* what will happen next in the reading. They *question* the information and the author of the text, *clarify* information and ideas, and *visualize* what the text is saying. Good readers also *summarize* the information that is presented and *make inferences* or *draw conclusions* about the facts and ideas.

I wish you well as you begin another school year. This *Science Notebook* is designed to help students understand the information in your Chemistry class. The guide will be a valuable tool that will also provide students with skills that they can use throughout their lives.

I hope you have a successful school year.

Sincerely,

Douglas Fisher

References

Faber, J. E., Morris, J. D., and Lieberman, M. G. (2000). The effect of note taking on ninth grade students' comprehension. *Reading Psychology*, 21, 257–270.

Ganske, L. (1981). Note-taking: A significant and integral part of learning environments. *Educational Communication and Technology: A Journal of Theory, Research, and Development*, 29, 155–175.

Martino, N. L., and Hoffman, P. R. (2002). An investigation of reading and language abilities of college freshmen. *Journal of Research in Reading*, 25, 310–318.

Pauk, W. (1974). How to Study in College. Boston: Houghton Mifflin.

Peverly, S. T., Brobst, K. E., Graham, M., Shaw, R. (2003). College adults are not good at self-regulation: A study on the relationship of self-regulation, note taking, and test taking. *Journal of Educational Psychology*, 95, 335–346.

Van Leeuwe, J., and Aarnoutse, C. (1998). Relation between reading comprehension, vocabulary, reading pleasure, and reading frequency. *Educational Research and Evaluation*, 4, 143–166.

Note-Taking Tips

Your notes are a reminder of what you learned in class. Taking good notes can help you succeed in science. The following tips will help you take better classroom notes.

- Before class, ask what your teacher will be discussing in class. Review mentally what you already know about the concept.
- Be an active listener. Focus on what your teacher is saying. Listen for important concepts. Pay attention to words, examples, and/or diagrams you teacher emphasizes.
- Write your notes as clear and concise as possible. The following symbols and abbreviations may be helpful in your note-taking.

Word or Phrase	Symbol or Abbreviation	Word or Phrase	Symbol or Abbreviation
for example	e.g.	and	+
that is	i.e.	approximately	≈
with	w/	therefore	∴
without	w/o	versus	vs

- Use a symbol such as a star (★) or an asterisk (*) to emphasize important concepts. Place a question mark (?) next to anything that you do not understand.
- Ask questions and participate in class discussion.
- Draw and label pictures or diagrams to help clarify a concept.
- When working out an example, write what you are doing to solve the problem next to each step. Be sure to use your own words.
- Review you notes as soon as possible after class. During this time, organize and summarize new concepts and clarify misunderstandings.

Note-Taking Don'ts

- **Don't** write every word. Concentrate on the main ideas and concepts.
- **Don't** use someone else's notes as they may not make sense.
- **Don't** doodle. It distracts you from listening actively.
- **Don't** lose focus or you will become lost in your note-taking.

Introduction to Chemistry

Before You Read

Before you read the chapter, write down four facts you know about chemistry.

1. Accept all reasonable responses. _____

2. _____

3. _____

4. _____

Science Journal

Write three questions about scientific methods and research.
Accept all reasonable responses. Possible answers include:

1. What is the difference between a hypothesis and a theory? _____

2. What is an independent variable? _____

3. What is a scientific law? _____

Introduction to Chemistry

Section 1.1 A Story of Two Substances

⟨**Main Idea**⟩ ———— ⟨**Details**⟩ ——————————————————

Scan *Section 1 of your text. Use the checklist below as a guide.*

- Read all section titles.
- Read all boldfaced words.
- Read all tables and graphs.
- Look at all pictures and read the captions.
- Think about what you already know about ozone and chloro-fluorocarbons (CFCs).

Write *four facts you discovered about ozone and chlorofluoro-carbons (CFCs).*

1. Accept all reasonable responses. _____

2. _____

3. _____

4. _____

⟨**New Vocabulary**⟩ *Use your text to define each term.*

chemistry   the study of matter and the changes that it undergoes

substance   matter that has a definite and uniform composition

Section 1.1 A Story of Two Substances (continued)

Main Idea —————

Details ————————————————————————

The Ozone Layer

Use with pages 5–7.

Explain *the ozone by completing the following paragraph.*

Overexposure to __ultraviolet radiation__ causes sunburn, is harmful

to __plants and animals__ , lowers __crop yields__ , and disrupts

__food chains__ . When __oxygen gas__ is exposed to ultraviolet radia-

tion in the upper regions of the __stratosphere__ , a chemical called

__ozone__ is formed. About __ninety percent__ of Earth's ozone

is spread out in a layer that surrounds and __protects__ our planet.

Ozone forms over the __equator__ and flows toward the __poles__ .

Sequence *the steps necessary for the formation of ozone.*

1. __Oxygen gas is exposed to ultraviolet radiation in the upper__

   __regions of the stratosphere.__

2. __The energy of the radiation breaks the gas particles into oxygen__

   __particles.__

3. __The oxygen particles interact with oxygen gas to form ozone.__

Illustrate *the balance between oxygen gas and ozone levels in the stratosphere, using Figure 1.3 in your text as a model. Give it a title and label the parts of your model.*

The Balance between Oxygen Gas and Ozone Levels in the Stratosphere

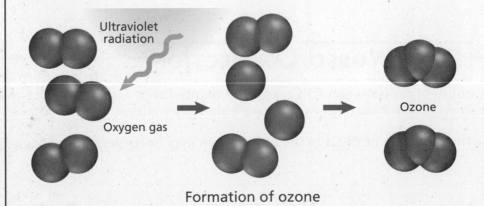

Ultraviolet radiation

Oxygen gas

Ozone

Formation of ozone

Name _____ Date _____

Section 1.1 A Story of Two Substances (continued)

Main Idea ——

Details ——

Chlorofluoro-carbons

Use with pages 7–8.

Analyze *the graph in Figure 1.6. Write a brief description of the concentration of CFCs from 1977 through 1996.*

Accept all reasonable responses. Students should demonstrate

that they recognize the correlation between the passage of time and

the rise in CFC levels.

Analyze *chlorofluorocarbons by completing the following table.*

CFCs Were First Developed Because:	Facts about CFCs	Uses of CFCs
The fumes from ammonia used as a coolant were harmful to people. Scientists began to look for safer coolants.	1. Several different chemicals are classified as CFCs. 2. They are all made in a laboratory. 3. They are non-toxic and stable. 4. They do not react readily with other chemicals. 5. They seemed to be ideal coolants for refrigerators.	refrigerants (for refrigerators and air conditioners) in plastic foams (such as foam cups) propellants in spray cans

REAL-WORLD CONNECTION

Infer from your reading the potential connection between CFCs and the ozone layer. Use Figure 1.5 and the table in the Section 1.1 Assessment to draw your conclusions.

The presence of CFCs in the atmosphere may be damaging the ozone layer.

_____

Introduction to Chemistry

Section 1.2 Chemistry and Matter

Main Idea ———— **Details** ————————————————

Skim *Section 2 of your text. Write four facts that come to mind from reading the headings, boldfaced words, and the illustration captions.*

1. Accept all reasonable responses.

2. _____

3. _____

4. _____

New Vocabulary   *Use your text to define each term.*

mass   a measurement that reflects the amount of matter

weight   a measure not only of the amount of matter but also of the effect of

Earth's gravitational pull on that matter

model   a visual, verbal, or mathematical explanation of experimental data

Section 1.2 Chemistry and Matter (continued)

Main Idea	Details

Matter and its Characteristics

Use with pages 9–10.

Compare and contrast *mass and weight using the Venn diagram below.*

- does not reflect gravitational pull on matter
- a measure of the effect of gravitational pull on matter
- a measurement that reflects the amount of matter in an object

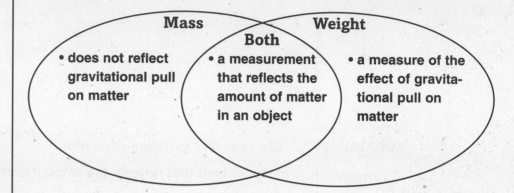

Mass
- does not reflect gravitational pull on matter

Both
- a measurement that reflects the amount of matter in an object

Weight
- a measure of the effect of gravitational pull on matter

Chemistry: The Central Science

Use with page 11.

Identify *six substances mentioned in the book that are important in everyday life and are made of chemicals.*

Accept all reasonable responses. Possible answers:

1. _____ fertilizers _____   4. _____ hair care products _____

2. _____ pesticides _____   5. _____ plastics _____

3. _____ building materials _____   6. _____ high-tech fabrics _____

Section 1.2 Chemistry and Matter (continued)

Main Idea ——   **Details** ————————————————

Organize *the following terms by arranging them from largest to smallest.*

macroscopic, submicroscopic, microscopic

macroscopic, microscopic, submicroscopic
_____

Explain *a chemical model by completing the following sentences.*

The ___**structure**___, composition, and ___**behavior**___ of all matter can be

explained on a ___**submicroscopic**___ level. All that we observe depends on

___**atoms**___ and the ___**changes**___ they undergo. ___**Chemistry**___ seeks to explain

the submicroscopic events that lead to ___**macroscopic observations**___.

One way to do this is by making a chemical model, a

___**visual representation**___ of a ___**submicroscopic event**___.

REAL-WORLD CONNECTION Analyze the importance of chemistry in our society using the branches of chemistry as examples.

Accept all reasonable answers. Possible answer: Without organic and inorganic chemistry,

we would not have the advances in medicine due to the development of life-saving

pharmaceuticals and delicate medical instruments. Physical chemistry has spurred the

development of conveniences like air conditioning, faster motors and more. Biochemistry

research helps detectives use DNA samples to solve crimes.

Introduction to Chemistry
Section 1.3 Scientific Methods

(Main Idea)	(Details)

Skim *Section 2 of your text. Write three questions that come to mind from reading the headings, boldface terms, and illustration captions.*

1. Accept all reasonable responses.

2. _____

3. _____

New Vocabulary) *Use your text to define each term.*

scientific method — a systematic approach used in scientific study, such as chemistry, biology, physics, or other sciences

hypothesis — a tentative, testable statement or prediction about what has been observed

experiment — a set of controlled observations that test the hypothesis

control — in an experiment, the standard that is used for comparison

conclusion — a judgment based on the information obtained

theory — an explanation that has been supported by many experiments

scientific law — describes a relationship in nature that is supported by many experiments

A Systematic Approach

Use with pages 12–15.

Compare *the terms qualitative data and quantitative data.*

Both are a type of observation that is used to gather information.

Qualitative data is descriptive and refers to how something looks, feels, sounds, tastes, or smells. Quantitative data is numerical and can be measured. It tells you how much, how little, how big, how tall, or how fast.

Section 1.3 Scientific Methods (continued)

Main Idea	Details

Compare *the terms independent variable and dependent variable.*

In an experiment, the experimenter changes the independent variable,

while the dependent variable is the variable whose value depends on

the independent variable.

Analyze *whether the characteristics listed below represent qualitative data, quantitative data, or both.*

Characteristic	Type of Data
the rate at which a candle burns	quantitative
a blanket with varying degrees of softness	both
sand with a reddish-brown color	qualitative

Sequence *the steps of the scientific method.*

__3__ Plan and set up one or more experiments to test one variable at a time.

__1__ Gather information using both qualitative data and quantitative data.

__4__ Observe, record, and analyze experimental data.

__2__ Develop a hypothesis, or tentative explanation based on observations.

__6__ Develop a theory or a scientific law.

__5__ Compare findings to the hypothesis, and form a conclusion.

Section 1.3 Scientific Methods (continued)

Main Idea ————

Use with page 15.

Details ——————————————

Analyze *Figure 1.13 and the caption information on Molina and Rowland's model. Explain in words what the model visually predicts about the effect of ultraviolet radiation on CFCs.*

Possible answer: Ultraviolet radiation breaks apart CFC molecules,

releasing chlorine atoms that would then strip the extra oxygen from

ozone molecules to form molecular oxygen.

_____

SYNTHESIZE

Design a simple experiment using the scientific method. Give your experiment a descriptive title. Limit the number of variables you test. Write the steps of the experiment based on the scientific method, including but not limited to hypothesis, analysis, and conclusions. Draw a simple sketch of your experiment, if appropriate, and label the independent, dependent, and control variables.

Title: Accept all reasonable responses._____

Steps: _____

_____

_____

_____

_____

_____

_____

_____

Independent variable(s): _____

Dependent variable(s): _____

Control variable(s): _____

Name _____ Date _____

Introduction to Chemistry
Section 1.4 Scientific Research

Main Idea ———— **Details** ————————————————

Skim *Section 4 of your text. Write three questions that come to mind from reading the headings, boldfaced terms, and illustration captions.*

1. Accept all reasonable responses. _____

2. _____

3. _____

New Vocabulary *Use your text to define each term.*

pure research   research that seeks to gain knowledge for the sake of knowledge itself

applied research   research undertaken to solve a specific problem

Academic Vocabulary *Define the following term.*

recover   to bring back to normal

Name_____ Date _____

Section 1.4 Scientific Research (continued)

Main Idea	Details

Types of Scientific Investigations

Use with pages 17–18.

Describe *scientific investigations by completing the following sentences.*

Pure research becomes __applied research__ when scientists develop a hypothesis based on the data and try to solve a specific problem.

__Chance discoveries__ have been made when a scientist reaches a conclusion far different than anticipated. Some wonderful scientific discoveries have been made __unexpectedly__.

Students in the Laboratory

Use with pages 18–19.

Review *Table 1.2 in your text. Write an A if you agree with the statement. Write a D if you disagree with the statement.*

__D__ Return unused chemicals to the stock bottle.

__A__ It is not safe to wear contact lenses in the lab.

__D__ Only a major accident, injury, incorrect procedure, or damage to equipment needs to be reported.

__D__ Graduated cylinders, burettes, or pipettes should be heated with a laboratory burner.

Analyze *laboratory safety by responding to the following situations.*

1. Explain in your own words why safety goggles and a laboratory apron must be worn whenever you are in the lab.

   Possible answer: Chemicals can splash and cause damage to eyes, skin, or clothing.

2. State why bare feet or sandals are not permitted in the lab.

   Possible answer: Chemicals may spill causing harm to the foot if it is not protected by a closed shoe.

Section 1.4 Scientific Research (continued)

Main Idea ——— **Details** —————————————————

3. Describe how you would explain to another student why you should not return unused chemicals to the stock bottle.

    Possible answer: The chemical may react with other chemicals in

    the environment and taint the pure chemical in the stock bottle,

    possibly even causing a reaction.

4. Explain why is it important to keep the balance area clean.

    Possible answer: Chemicals that were not cleaned up may cause

    an adverse reaction.

SYNTHESIZE Some students are conducting an experiment that involves combining sodium and water. Too much sodium is added, which causes a fire. A student reacts by throwing water on the fire, but this only causes the fire to spread. The teacher finally puts the fire out. Based on what you now know about chemistry and lab safety, explain how this could have been avoided.

Accept all reasonable responses. Possible answer: This could have been avoided by studying

the lab assignment and using the correct amount of each chemical as well as by using a fire

blanket to douse the fire rather than water. Once it occurred the teacher should have been

alerted immediately.

Introduction to Chemistry Chapter Wrap-Up

Now that you have read the chapter, review what you have learned. Fill in the blanks below with the correct word or phrase.

Chemistry is the study of **matter and the changes that it undergoes** .

Matter is anything that has **mass** and takes up **space** . Mass is **a measurement of the amount of matter** and differs from weight in that it does not measure the effect of **gravitational pull** on matter.

The steps of the scientific process include:

making observations, formulating a hypothesis, doing experiments,

forming a conclusion, and developing a theory or scientific law

Two types of scientific investigation are:

pure research and applied research

Review

Use this checklist to help you study.

☐ Study your Science Notebook for this chapter.

☐ Study the vocabulary words and scientific definitions.

☐ Review daily homework assignments.

☐ Reread the chapter and review the tables, graphs, and illustrations.

☐ Review the Section Assessment questions at the end of each section.

☐ Look over the Study Guide at the end of the chapter.

REAL-WORLD CONNECTION

Explain three ways you use chemistry in daily life. Accept all reasonable responses. Possible answers:

1. **Chemistry is involved anytime you bake.**

2. **Air fresheners cause a reaction that eliminates odors.**

3. **The performance of your car may depend on the type of gas.**

Analyzing Data
Before You Read

Review Vocabulary   *Define the following terms.*

qualitative data   **information that describes color, odor, shape, or some other physical characteristic**

quantitative data   **numerical information that tells you how much, how little, how big, how tall, or how fast**

variable   **a quantity or condition that can have more than one value**

analysis   **the separating of a thing or idea into its parts to find out their nature, proportion, function, or interrelationship**

Chapter 1   *You and a friend are making sweetened iced tea. You both have different opinions about how much sugar to add and at what temperature is best to add the sugar. Design an experiment to find out how much sugar will dissolve at three different temperatures. In your experiment, identify the following:*
Answers may vary for experiments.

Qualitative data   **the appearance of the sugar as it dissolves**

Quantitative data   **the amount of sugar that dissolves at each temperature; temperature**

Independent variable   **the temperature of the tea**

Dependent variable   **the amount of sugar that dissolves at each temperature**

Analyzing Data
Section 2.1 Units and Measurements

(Main Idea) _____   **(Details)** _____

Skim *Section 1 of your text. Write a question you have about each of the two types of units discussed in this section.*

1. <u>Accept all reasonable responses.</u>

2. _____

New Vocabulary   *Use your text to define each term.*

base unit   <u>a defined unit in a system of measurement that is based on an object</u>

<u>or event in the physical world</u>

derived unit   <u>a unit that is defined by a combination of base units</u>

density   <u>a ratio that compares the mass of an object to its volume</u>

Match *the SI base units below with their functions.*

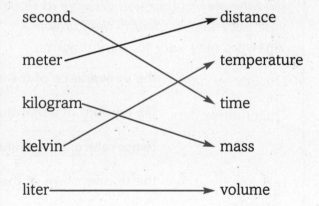

Section 2.1 Units and Measurements (continued)

Main Idea ———— **Details** ————————————————————————

Units

Use with page 32.

Identify *five items around your home that use SI units of measurement.*

1. _Accept all reasonable responses._____

2. _____

3. _____

4. _____

5. _____

Base Units and SI Prefixes

Use with pages 33–35.

Organize *these prefixes from smallest to largest.*

_1_ pico   _9_ giga

_3_ micro   _2_ nano

_6_ deci   _4_ milli

_7_ kilo   _5_ centi

_8_ mega

Temperature

Use with pages 34–35.

Compare and contrast *the kelvin scale and the Celsius scale.*

Answers will vary. Both scales have a range of one hundred between the freezing point

and the boiling point of water. Celsius sets the freezing point at 0° and the boiling point

at 100°. The freezing point for kelvin is 273 K and the boiling point is 373 K.

Derived Units

Use with pages 35–37.

Explain *density by completing the following statement and equation.*

Density is a _ratio_ that _compares_ the _mass_ of an object to its _volume_.

$$\text{density} = \frac{\text{mass}}{\text{volume}}$$

Section 2.1 Units and Measurements (continued)

Main Idea

Using Density and Volume to Find Mass

Use with Example Problem 2.1, page 38.

Details

Solve *Read Example Problem 2.1 in your text.*

You Try It

Problem ---------------------------

Determine the mass of an object that, when placed in a 25-mL graduated cylinder containing 14 mL of water, causes the level of the water to rise to 19 mL. The object has a density of 3.2 g/mL.

1. Analyze the Problem

Known: density = 3.2 g/mL, volume = 5.0 mL

Unknown: mass = ? g

You know the density and the volume of an object and must determine its mass; therefore, you will calculate the answer using the density equation.

2. Solve for the Unknown

Write the density equation.

$$\text{density} = \frac{\text{mass}}{\text{volume}}$$

Rearrange the density equation to solve for mass.

mass = volume × density

Substitute the known values for **volume** and **density** into the equation.

mass = 5.0 mL × 3.2 g/mL

Multiply the values and units. The mL units will cancel out.

$$\text{mass} = \underline{5.0 \text{ mL}} \times \underline{3.2 \text{ g/mL}} = \underline{16 \text{ g}}$$

3. Evaluate the Answer

The two sides of the equation should be **equal**.

density = **mass ÷ volume**

3.2 g/mL = 16 g/5.0 mL

If you divide 16 g by 5.0 mL, you get **3.2 g/mL**

Analyzing Data

Section 2.2 Scientific Notation and Dimensional Analysis

⊂Main Idea⊃ ——— **⊂Details⊃** ———————————————

Scan *Section 2 of your text. Use the checklist below as a guide.*

• Read all section titles.

• Read all boldfaced words.

• Read all tables and graphs.

• Look at all pictures and read the captions.

• Think about what you already know about this subject.

Write *three facts you discovered about scientific notation and dimensional analysis.*

1. **Accept all reasonable responses.** _____

2. _____

3. _____

New⌐
⊂Vocabulary⌐ *Use your text to define each term.*

scientific notation **expresses numbers as a multiple of two factors: a number**

between one and ten; and ten raised to a power, or exponent

dimensional analysis **a method of problem-solving that focuses on the units used to**

describe matter

conversion factor **a ratio of equivalent values having different units**

Academic⌐
⊂Vocabulary⌐ *Define the following term.*

sum **the whole amount; the result of adding numbers**

Section 2.2 Scientific Notation and Dimensional Analysis (continued)

⟨ Main Idea ⟩ ——————— ⟨ Details ⟩ ——————————————————————————————————

Scientific Notation

Use with Example Problem 2.2, page 41.

Solve *Read Example Problem 2.2 in your text.*

You Try It

• Problem ——-——-——-——-——-——-——-——-——-——-——-——-——-——•

Change the following data into scientific notation:

a. The distance between Pluto and the Sun is 5, 913, 000 km.

b. The density of nitrogen gas, a major component of Pluto's atmosphere, is .0012506 g/cm^3.

1. Analyze the Problem

Known: distance = 5, 913, 000 km and density = 0.0012506 g/cm

Unknown: **scientific notation**

You are given two measurements. In both cases, the answers will be factors between 1 and 10 that are multiplied by a power of ten.

2. Solve for the Unknown

Move the decimal point to produce a factor between 1 and 10. Count the number of places the decimal point moved and the direction.

5, 913, 000	**0.0012506**
The decimal point moved	*The decimal point moved*
__6__ *places to the* __left__.	__3__ *places to the* __right__.

Remove the extra zeros at the end or beginning of the factor.

Multiply the result by 10^n where n equals the __number of places moved__. When the decimal point moves to the left, n is a __positive__ number. When the decimal point moves to the right, n is a __negative__ number. Remember to add units to the answers.

a. __5.913 × 10^6 km__

b. __1.2506 × 10^{-3} g/cm^3__

3. Evaluate the Answer

The answers have __two__ factors. The first factor is a number between __1__ and __10__. In answer a, because the distance to Pluto is a large number, 10 has a __positive exponent__. In answer b, because the density of nitrogen gas is a very small number, the exponent is __negative__.

Section 2.2 Scientific Notation and Dimensional Analysis (continued)

Main Idea	Details

Using Conversion Factors

Use with Example Problem 2.4, page 46.

Solve *Read Example Problem 2.4 in your text.*

You Try It

Problem

The Cassini probe heading toward Saturn will reach speeds of 5.2 kilometers per second. How many meters per minute would it travel at this speed?

1. **Analyze the Problem**

   Known: **speed of 5.2 kilometers per second**

   Unknown: **the equivalent speed in meters per minute**

   You need conversion factors that relate kilometers to meters and seconds to minutes. A conversion factor is a **ratio** of **equivalent values** used to express **the same quantity** in **different units** .

2. **Solve for the Unknown**

   First convert kilometers to meters. Set up the conversion factor so that the kilometer units will cancel out.

   $$\frac{5.2 \text{ km}}{\text{s}} \times \frac{1000 \text{ m}}{1 \text{ km}} = \frac{\textbf{5200 m}}{\text{s}}$$

   Next convert seconds to minutes. Set up the conversion factor so that the seconds will cancel out.

   $$\frac{5200 \text{ m}}{\text{s}} \times \frac{60 \text{ s}}{1 \text{ min}} = \frac{\textbf{312,000 m}}{\text{min}}$$

3. **Evaluate the Answer**

   To check your answer, you can do the steps in reverse order.

   $$\frac{5.2 \text{ km}}{\text{s}} \times \frac{60 \text{ s}}{1 \text{ min}} = \frac{312 \text{ km}}{\text{min}} \times \frac{1000 \text{ m}}{\text{min}} = \frac{\textbf{312,000 km}}{\text{min}}$$

Analyzing Data
Section 2.3 Uncertainty in Data

Main Idea ——————   **Details** ————————————————

Skim *Section 3 of your text. Focus on the headings, subheadings, boldfaced words, and main ideas. Summarize the main ideas of this section.*

_____

_____

_____

_____

New Vocabulary   *Use your text to define each term.*

accuracy   how close a measured value is to an accepted value

precision   how close a series of measurements are to one another

error   the difference between an experimental value and an accepted value

percent error   ratio of an error to an accepted value

significant figure   include all known digits plus one estimated digit

Section 2.3 Uncertainty in Data (continued)

⟨Main Idea⟩ ——	⟨Details⟩ —————————————————————

⟨Main Idea⟩

Error and Percent Error

Use with pages 48–49.

Calculating Percent Error

Use with Example Problem 2.5, page 49.

⟨Details⟩

Explain *percent error by completing the statement and equation below.*

Percent error is the <u>ratio</u> of an <u>error</u> to an <u>accepted value</u>.

$$\text{Percent error} = \frac{\text{error}}{\text{accepted value}} \times \underline{100}$$

Solve *Read Example Problem 2.5 in your text.*

You Try It

Problem –––––––––––––––––––––––––––––––––––––•

Calculate the percent errors. Report your answers to two places after the decimal point. The table below summarizes Student B's data.

Trial	Density(g/cm³)	Error(g/cm³)
1	1.4	−0.19
2	1.68	0.09
3	1.45	0.14

1. Analyze the Problem

Known: <u>The accepted value for density of sucrose is 1.59 g/cm.</u>

<u>The errors are –0.19 g/cm, 0.09 g/cm, and –0.14 g/cm.</u>

Unknown: <u>the percent error</u>

Use the accepted value for density and the errors to calculate percent error.

2. Solve for the Unknown

Substitute each error into the percent error equation.

$$\text{percent error} = \frac{\text{error}}{\text{accepted value}} \times 100$$

$$\text{percent error} = \frac{-0.19 \text{ g/cm}^3}{1.59 \text{ g/cm}^3} \times 100 = \boxed{11.94\%}$$

$$\text{percent error} = \frac{0.09 \text{ g/cm}^3}{1.59 \text{ g/cm}^3} \times 100 = \boxed{5.66\%}$$

$$\text{percent error} = \frac{-0.14 \text{ g/cm}^3}{1.59 \text{ g/cm}^3} \times 100 = \boxed{8.81\%}$$

3. Evaluate the Answer

The percent error is greatest for trial <u>1</u> which had the largest error, and smallest for trial <u>2</u> which was closest to the accepted value.

Section 2.3 Uncertainty in Data (continued)

(Main Idea)	(Details)

Significant Figures

Use with page 50.

Identify *the significant numbers below by drawing a circle around them. Use the five rules for recognizing significant digits on page 51 for reference.*

0.0<u>25</u>   <u>325, 078</u>   <u>56</u> 00

Rounding Numbers

Use with page 52.

Explain *the rules for rounding numbers by completing the following sentences. Then complete the example of each rule for rounding numbers.*

1. If the digit to the immediate right of the last significant figure is less than five, <u>do not change the last significant figure.</u>

   3.751 <u>= 3.75</u>

2. If the digit to the immediate right of the last significant figure is greater than five, <u>round up the last significant figure.</u>

   4.127 <u>= 4.13</u>

3. If the digit to the immediate right of the last significant figure is equal to five and is followed by a nonzero digit, <u>round up the last significant figure.</u>

   8.3253 <u>= 8.33</u>

4. If the digit to the immediate right of the last significant figure is equal to five and is not followed by a nonzero digit, look at the last significant figure. <u>If it is an odd digit, round it up. If it is an even digit, do not round up.</u>

   1.4750 = <u>1.48</u> ;1.4650 = <u>1.46</u>

Analyzing Data
Section 2.4 Representing Data

<Main Idea>——— <Details>———————————————————————

Scan *Section 4 of your text. Use the checklist below as a guide.*

- Read all section titles.

- Read all tables and graphs.

- Look at all pictures and read the captions.

- Think about what you already know about data analysis.

Write *facts you learned about representing data as you scanned the section.*

1. Accept all reasonable responses._____

2. _____

3. _____

<New Vocabulary> *Use your text to define the following term.*

graph a visual display of data _____

Section 2.4 Representing Data (continued)

⟨**Main Idea**⟩——— ⟨**Details**⟩——————————————

Graphing

Use with pages 55–56.

Draw *and label (a) a circle graph and (b) a bar graph using the information in the table below.*

Student Budget	
Budget items	**Percent**
Car insurance	45
Movies	6
Books	5
Clothing	30
Miscellaneous	4
Gas	10

Student Budget bar graph   Student Budget circle graph

The ___circle graph___ best displays the data in the Student Budget

table because ___it shows the relationship of each item___

___as part of a whole_____.

Name_____ Date_____

Section 2.4 Representing Data (continued)

Main Idea	Details

Line Graphs

Use with pages 56–57.

Identify *each of the following slopes.*

__positive__ slope   __negative__ slope

Analyze *whether the following sequences will likely plot as linear or nonlinear relationships.*

Sequence A: **Sequence B:**
Result 1: 2   Result A: 31
Result 2: 4   Result B: 27
Result 3: 7   Result C: 49
Result 4: 10   Result D: 45

Answer: __linear__   Answer: __nonlinear__

Interpreting Graphs

Use with pages 57–58.

Organize *information about interpreting graphs by completing the sentences below.*

Information on a graph typically consists of __two__ types of variables: __independent__ variables and __dependent__ variables.

The relationship between the variables may reflect either a __positive__ or a __negative__ slope.

When reading the graph, you use either interpolation for __data that falls between measured points__ or __extrapolation__ for estimated values beyond the plotted points.

Analyzing Data Chapter Wrap-Up

Now that you have read the chapter, review what you have learned. Write out the key equations and relationships.

$$density = \frac{mass}{volume}$$

$$percent\ error = \frac{error}{accepted\ value} \times 100$$

$$slope = \frac{y_2 - y_1}{x_2 - x_1} = \frac{\Delta y}{\Delta x}$$

Conversion between temperature scales:

$$°C + \underline{273} = \underline{K}$$

$$K - \underline{273} = \underline{°C}$$

Review | *Use this checklist to help you study.*

☐ Study your Science Notebook for this chapter.

☐ Study the definitions of vocabulary words.

☐ Review daily homework assignments.

☐ Reread the chapter and review the tables, graphs, and illustrations.

☐ Review the Section Assessment questions at the end of each section.

☐ Look over the Study Guide at the end of the chapter.

SUMMARIZE

If you were a scientist, what precautionary guidelines would you use to ensure the accuracy of your data and to provide a clear representation of that data?

Accept all reasonable responses. Guidelines might include consistent use of SI units, proper

conversion of data into scientific notation, taking accurate and precise measurements, proper

rounding of numbers, and representing data in the most advantageous manner for proper analysis.

Matter—Properties and Changes

Before You Read

Define the following terms.

matter | anything that has mass and takes up space

significant figure | all known digits plus one estimated digit

Chapter 2

Measure *the height and arm length for five friends or family members. In the space below, create an appropriate graph to represent the data you collected.* Accept all reasonable responses.

Compare and contrast *circle, bar and line graphs.*

A circle graph is divided into wedges and is useful for showing parts

of a fixed whole. The parts are usually labeled as percents. A bar

graph is useful for showing how a quantity varies with factors, such

as time, location, or temperature. The quantity being measured

appears on the vertical axis (y-axis). The independent variable

appears on the horizontal axis (x-axis). The points on a line graph

represent the intersection of data for two variables. The independent

variable is plotted on the horizontal axis (x-axis). The dependent

variable is plotted on the vertical axis (y-axis).

Matter—Properties and Changes

Section 3.1 Properties of Matter

Main Idea ———— **Details** ——————————————————————

Skim *Section 1 of your text. Write three questions that come to mind from reading the headings and the illustration captions.*

1. Accept all reasonable responses._____

2. _____

3. _____

New Vocabulary *Use your text to define each term.*

states of matter | the physical forms of all matter on Earth

vapor | the gaseous state of a substance that is a solid or liquid at room temperature

physical property | a characteristic that can be observed or measured without changing the sample's composition

extensive property | physical property that is dependent on the amount of a substance present

intensive property | physical property that is independent of the amount of a substance present

chemical property | the ability of a substance to combine with or change into one or more other substances

Match *each of the following states of matter with its physical description*

solid ⟍ ⟋ flows and fills the entire volume of its container

liquid ⟍✕⟋ has definite shape and volume

gas ⟋ ⟍ flows and has a constant volume

Academic Vocabulary *Define the following term.*

resource | a source of information or expertise

Section 3.1 Properties of Matter (continued)

Main Idea ——— **Details** ————————————————————

States of Matter

Use with pages 71–72.

Compare *the way the three common states of matter fill a container.*

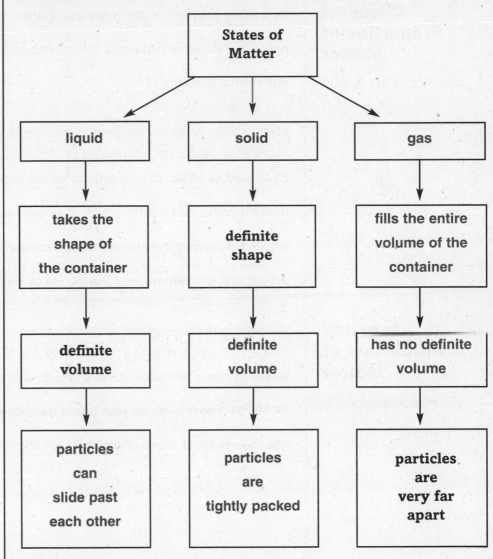

REAL-WORLD CONNECTION Meteorologists (scientists who study weather) refer to water in the gaseous state in the atmosphere as water vapor. Explain why this term is used.

The word gas is used for a substance that is in that state at room temperature. Vapor is used

for a gaseous substance that is normally a liquid at room temperature.

_____

Section 3.1 Properties of Matter (continued)

⌐Main Idea⌐	⌐Details⌐

Physical and Chemical Properties of Matter

Use with pages 73–74.

Contrast *intensive and extensive physical properties.*

Extensive properties are dependent upon the amount of a substance

present. Intensive products are independent of the amount of

substance present.

List *several physical properties and explain why they are used more than chemical properties in the identification of objects.*

Examples of physical properties include density, color, odor, hardness,

melting point, and boiling point. These are easy to observe or test

without changing the sample's composition. To observe chemical

properties, a chemical reaction needs to be observed.

Observing Properties of Matter

Use with pages 74–75.

Compare *the properties of water at room temperature with water that has a temperature greater than 100°C.*

Water at room temperature is a liquid with a density of 1.00 g/cm^3.

At 100°C, water is a gas and has a density of 0.0006 g/cm^3. The

gaseous state is more chemically reactive than the liquid state.

Matter—Properties and Changes

Section 3.2 Changes in Matter

Main Idea

Details

Scan *Section 2 of your text. Use the checklist below as a guide.*

- Read all section titles.
- Read all boldfaced words.
- Read all tables and graphs.
- Look at all pictures and read the captions.
- Think about what you already know about this subject.

Write *three facts you discovered about changes in matter.*

1. Accept all reasonable responses. _____

2. _____

3. _____

New Vocabulary   *Use your text to define each term.*

physical change change in a substance that does not alter its composition

phase change a transition of matter from one state to another

chemical change when one or more substances change into a new substance

law of conservation of mass states that mass is neither created nor destroyed during a

chemical reaction

Section 3.2 Changes in Matter (continued)

Main Idea	Details

Physical and Chemical Changes

Use with pages 76–77.

Determine *which type of change each statement represents. Use P for physical change and C for chemical change. Explain your answers.*

silver spoon tarnishes **C**

Explanation: **a new substance, tarnish, is created**

crushing an aluminum can **P**

Explanation: **only the shape of the can changes**

freezing water **P**

Explanation: **only the state of matter changes**

burning wood **C**

Explanation: **a new substance, ash, is created**

copper turns a greenish color **C**

Explanation: **a new substance is created**

grind coffee beans **P**

Explanation: **only the size and shape of the beans change**

Describe *how iron turns into a brownish-red powder. Name the reactants and product that are involved*

Iron reacts with oxygen in the air to form rust. The reactants are iron

and oxygen. The product is rust.

_____

_____

_____

Section 3.2 Changes in Matter (continued)

Main Idea

Details

Conservation of Mass

Use with Example Problem 3.1, page 78.

Summarize *Fill in the blanks to help you take notes while you read Example Problem 3.1.*

• **Problem**

The total __mass__ of the products must __equal__ the total mass of the __reactants__. This shows the law of __conservation of mass__.

1. **Analyze the Problem**

   Known: mass of mercury(II) oxide = 10.00 g, mass of

   liquid mercury = 9.26 g

   Unknown: mass of oxygen formed

2. **Solve for the Unknown**

   Write an equation showing conservation of mass of reactants and products.

   mass of **mercury(II) oxide** = mass of **mercury** + mass of **oxygen**

   Write an equation to solve for the mass of oxygen.

   mass of **oxygen** = mass of **mercury(II) oxide** − mass of **mercury**

   Substitute known values and solve.

   Mass of oxygen = __10.00__ g − __9.26__ g

   Mass oxygen = __0.74__ g

3. **Evaluate the Answer**

   Write an equation that shows mass of the two products equals the mass of the reactant.

   __9.26__ g mercury + __0.74__ g oxygen = __10.00__ g mercury(II) oxide

Matter—Properties and Changes
Section 3.3 Mixtures of Matter

Main Idea ———   **Details** ———————————

Scan *Section 3 of your text. Use the checklist below as a guide.*

- Read all section titles.
- Read all boldfaced words.
- Read all charts and graphs.
- Look at all pictures and read the captions.

List *three facts you have learned about mixtures.*

1. Accept all reasonable responses. _____

2. _____

3. _____

New Vocabulary   *Use your text to find the correct term for each definition.*

mixture	a combination of two or more pure substances in which each substance retains its individual chemical properties
heterogeneous mixture	a mixture in which the individual substances remain distinct
homogeneous mixture	a mixture that has a constant composition throughout
solution	another word for a homogeneous mixture
filtration	a technique that uses a porous barrier to separate a solid from a liquid
distillation	separation technique that is based on differences in the boiling points of the substances involved
crystallization	separation technique resulting in the formation of pure solid substances from a solution containing the dissolved substance
sublimation	process during which a solid changes to a vapor without melting
chromatography	technique that separates the components of a mixture based on differing tendencies to move across the surface of another substance

Section 3.3 Mixtures of Matter (continued)

| Main Idea | Details |

Mixtures

Use with pages 80–81.

Describe *how mixtures relate to substances.*

A mixture is a combination of two or more pure substances. In a

mixture, each substance retains its individual chemical properties.

Contrast *heterogeneous and homogeneous mixtures.*

Homogeneous mixtures have constant composition throughout and

are in a single phase. Heterogeneous mixtures do not blend smoothly

throughout. The individual substances of the mixture remain distinct.

Describe *what an alloy is and why alloys are used.*

Alloys are homogeneous mixtures of metals. The properties of the

different metals combine to improve strength and durability of the product.

Separating Mixtures

Use with pages 82–83.

Identify *four techniques that take advantage of different physical properties in order to separate mixtures and describe how each is done.*

Technique 1: filtration

How it is done: a porous barrier is used to separate a solid from a liquid

Technique 2: distillation

How it is done: a mixture is heated until the substance with the

lowest boiling point becomes a vapor and can then be condensed

into a liquid and collected

Technique 3: crystallization

How it is done: a solution containing as much dissolved substance

as it can possibly hold will have dissolved substance come out of

solution and form crystals if a tiny amount more is added

Section 3.3 Mixtures of Matter (continued)

Main Idea ———— **Details** ————————————————

Technique 4: **chromatography**

How it is done: **components of a mixture separate as they spread through another material at different rates**

Sequence *the steps of separating a mixture of sand, salt, and iron filings. Identify which physical property you were using in each step.*

2 Mix the sand and salt mixture with water.

Physical property used: **salt dissolves in water, sand does not dissolve in the water**

4 Boil the salt and water mixture, leaving the salt behind.

Physical property used:

Water evaporates and salt is left behind as a residue.

1 Separate the iron filings from the sand and salt by using a magnet.

Physical property used: **Iron filings are attracted by a magnet. Salt and sand are not.**

3 Use filtration to separate the sand from the salt and water.

Physical property used: **The filter paper will not let the sand pass through it. The water-salt solution will pass through the filter paper.**

REAL-WORLD CONNECTION Crude oil (petroleum) is a mixture of several materials, including gasoline, kerosene, diesel fuel, and heating oil. Describe whether you think distillation or filtration would be a better method to separate the products of crude oil. Hint: each of the products listed has a different boiling point.

Filtration is used to separate a solid from a liquid. The products listed are liquids and all have different boiling points, so each can be separated out through distillation.

Matter—Properties and Changes

Section 3.4 Elements and Compounds

Main Idea — | **Details** _____

Scan *Section 4 of your text. Review the periodic table of elements. Record some observations about how the table is organized and what information you can determine just by looking at the table.* **Accept all reasonable responses.**

_____

_____

_____

New Vocabulary | *Use your text to define each term.*

element | a pure substance that cannot be separated into simpler substances

by physical or chemical means

periodic table | table organizing the elements into rows called periods and columns

called groups

compound | a combination of two or more different elements that are

chemically combined

law of definite proportions | states that a compound is always composed of the same elements in

the same proportions by mass

percent by mass | the ratio of the mass of each element in a compound to the total

mass of the compound

law of multiple proportions | states that when different compounds are formed by a combination of the

same elements, different masses of one element combine with the same

relative mass of the other element in a ratio of small whole numbers

Section 3.4 Elements and Compounds (continued)

Main Idea ———   **Details** ————————————————

Elements and Compounds

Use with pages 84–87.

Discuss *elements and compounds by completing the following paragraph.*

There are __92__ naturally occurring elements. Seventy-five percent of the universe is __hydrogen__ . The Earth's crust and the human body are made of different elements. But __oxygen__ is an element that is abundant in both. Most objects are made of __compounds__ with approximately ten million known and over __100,000__ being developed and discovered every __year__ .

Analyze *the concept map for matter in Figure 3.19. Write a brief description of the information the concept map is conveying.*

The concept map is showing how elements, compounds, substances,

and mixtures define all matter.

_____

_____

Describe *how the periodic table organizes elements.*

The periodic table organizes the elements into a grid of horizontal rows

called periods and vertical columns called groups or families. Elements

in the same group have similar chemical and physical properties.

_____

Explain *how Figure 3.18 illustrates the fact that the properties of a compound are different from the properties of its component elements.*

Sodium is a highly reactive element that fizzes and burns when

added to water. Chlorine is a poisonous, pale green gas. However,

these elements combine to form sodium chloride, which is a white,

unreactive solid used to flavor foods.

Section 3.4 Elements and Compounds (continued)

| Main Idea | Details |

Law of Definite Proportions

Use with pages 87–88.

Describe *how to do percent by mass by completing the following paragraph.*

The __mass__ of a compound is __equal__ to the __sum__ of the masses of the __elements__ that make up the compound. This demonstrates the law of __conservation of matter__.

Analyze *the law of definite proportions by indicating whether the following examples are for identical or different compounds.*

Description	Analysis
Compound 1 consists of 24g of Na, and 36g of Cl. Compound 2 has 36g of Na and 54g of Cl.	**identical compounds**
Compound 3 has 10.00g of lead and 1.55g of sulfur. Compound 4 has 10.00 g of lead, 1.55g of sulfur, and 1.55g of carbon.	**different compounds**

Law of Multiple Proportions

Use with pages 89–90.

Describe *the law of multiple proportions by completing the following statement.*

When different __compounds__ are formed by combining the same __elements__, different masses of one element combine with the same __relative mass__ of the other element in a ratio of __small whole numbers__.

SYNTHESIZE

Carbon combines with oxygen to form two compounds, carbon monoxide and carbon dioxide. Based on the law of multiple proportions, describe how the proportions of oxygen in the two compounds relate to each other.

The amount of oxygen in carbon monoxide will compare to the amount of oxygen in carbon dioxide in a small whole number ratio.

Matter—Properties and Changes Chapter Wrap-Up

After reading this chapter, list three things you have learned about the properties and changes in matter.

1. <u>Accept all reasonable responses.</u>_____

2. _____

3. _____

Review

Use this checklist to help you study.

☐ Use this Science Notebook to study this chapter.

☐ Study the vocabulary words and scientific definitions.

☐ Review daily homework assignments.

☐ Reread the chapter and review the tables, graphs, and illustrations.

☐ Review the Section Assessment questions at the end of each section.

☐ Look over the Study Guide at the end of the chapter.

REAL-WORLD CONNECTION

Explain how understanding the physical and chemical properties of matter can help find alternatives to the burning of fossil fuels, thus reducing the amount of harmful greenhouse gases released into the atmosphere.

<u>Accept all reasonable responses. Possible answer: Greenhouse gases are generated through</u>

<u>chemical reactions. By understanding chemical properties, researchers and engineers can</u>

<u>predict the reactions that will cause greenhouse gases, and take steps to avoid them during</u>

<u>product design and development.</u>

_____

The Structure of the Atom

Before You Read

Review Vocabulary *Define the following terms.*

scientific law	describes a relationship in nature that is supported by many experiments
theory	an explanation supported by many experiments; is still subject to new experimental data, can be modified, and is considered successful if it can be used to make predictions that are true
element	a pure substance that cannot be separated into simpler substances by physical or chemical means
law of definite proportions	states that regardless of the amount, a compound is always composed of the same elements in the same proportion by mass
law of multiple proportions	states that when different compounds are formed by a combination of the same elements, different masses of one element combine with the same mass of the other element in a ratio of small whole numbers

Describe *three things that you already know about the atom.*

1. Accept all reasonable responses.

2. _____

3. _____

The Structure of the Atom
Section 4.1 Early Ideas About Matter

⸨Main Idea⸩ ——— **⸨Details⸩** ————————————————

Scan *Section 1 of your text. Use the checklist below as a guide.*

• Read all section titles.

• Read all boldfaced words.

• Read all tables and graphs.

• Look at all pictures and read the captions.

• Think about what you already know about this subject.

List *three things you expect to learn about while reading the section.*

1. Accept all reasonable responses._____

2. _____

3. _____

⸨New Vocabulary⸩ *Use your text to define each term.*

Dalton's atomic theory a theory proposed by John Dalton in 1808, based on numerous

scientific experiments, which marked the beginning of the

development of modern atomic theory

Section 4.1 Early Ideas About Matter (continued)

Main Idea ———— **Details** ——————————————————————

Greek Philosophers

Use with pages 102–103.

Summarize *the effect that Aristotle had on the atomic theory proposed by Democritus.*

Aristotle rejected Democritus's ideas because they did not agree with his ideas

on nature. He did not believe that the "nothingness" of empty space could

exist. He denied the existence of atoms. People accepted Aristotle's

conclusions for 2,000 years, and the ideas of Democritus were not developed.

John Dalton

Use with page 104.

List *the main points of Dalton's atomic theory.*

1. All matter is composed of extremely small particles called atoms.

2. All atoms of a given element are identical in size, mass, and chemical properties. Atoms of one element are different from those atoms of any other element.

3. Atoms cannot be created, divided into smaller particles, or destroyed.

4. Different atoms combine in simple whole-number ratios to form compounds.

5. In a chemical reaction, atoms are separated, combined, or rearranged.

Discuss *Dalton's ideas by completing the following paragraph.*

After years of studying __chemical reactions__, Dalton was able to

accurately determine the __mass ratios__ of the elements involved

in the reactions. His conclusions resulted in the __atomic theory__,

which helped to explain that __atoms__ in chemical reactions

separate, __combine__, or __rearrange__, but are not created,

__destroyed__, or __divided__.

Section 4.1 Early Ideas About Matter (continued)

⟨Main Idea⟩ —— ⟨Details⟩ ————————————————————————

Compare and contrast *the atomic theories of Democritus and Dalton. Mark an X under each name if a statement in the table applies to that person's theory.*

Statement	Democritus	Dalton
All matter is made of tiny pieces.	X	X
Matter is made of empty space through which atoms move.	X	
Atoms cannot be divided.	X	X
Atoms cannot be created.	X	X
Atoms cannot be destroyed.	X	X
Different atoms combine in whole-number ratios to form compounds.		X
The properties of atoms vary based on shape, size, and movement.	X	
Different kinds of atoms come in different sizes and shapes.	X	

REAL-WORLD CONNECTION The experiments of the alchemists revealed the properties of some metals and provided the foundation for the science of chemistry. Although not successful, alchemy proved beneficial to science. Explain how this example can be applied to modern research.

Accept all reasonable responses. Possible answer: Even research and experiments that do

not succeed add to our body of knowledge and provide useful information to later

researchers.

The Structure of the Atom
Section 4.2 Defining the Atom

⌐Main Idea⌐ ———— **⌐Details⌐** ————————————————

Scan *Section 2 of your text. Use the checklist below as a guide.*

- Read all section titles.
- Read all boldfaced words.
- Read all tables and graphs.
- Look at all pictures and read the captions.
- Think about what you already know about this subject.

Write *two facts you discovered about subatomic particles.*

1. Accept all reasonable responses._____

2. _____

⌐New Vocabulary⌐ *Use your text to define each term.*

cathode ray ray of radiation emitting from the cathode end of a tube used by

researchers to study mass and charge

electron negatively charged particles that are part of all forms of matter

nucleus tiny, dense, centrally located region within the atom that contains all of

an atom's positive charge and virtually all of its mass

proton a subatomic particle carrying a charge equal to but opposite that of an

electron; that is, a positive charge of 1+

neutron a subatomic particle with a mass nearly equal to that of a proton,

but that has no electrical charge

The Atom

Use with pages 106–107.

Explain *an atom by completing the following statements.*

The atom is the smallest particle that retains the properties

of the element_____.

When a group of atoms ___bond together___ and act as a

___unit___, the result is known as a ___molecule___.

Section 4.2 Defining the Atom (continued)

⟨**Main Idea**⟩———— ⟨**Details**⟩—————————————————

The Electron

Use with pages 107–110.

Summarize *the information you learned from cathode ray experiments. Use Figure 4.7 for reference.*

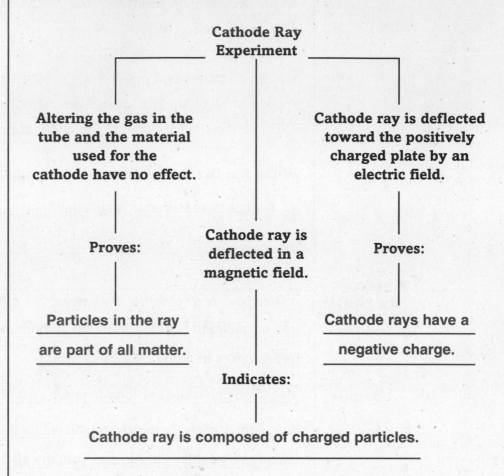

Identify *the major discoveries about subatomic particles made by the 19th century.*

1. Cathode rays were actually a stream of charged particles.

2. The particles carried a negative charge.

3. There were particles smaller than atoms.

Section 4.2 Defining the Atom (continued)

Main Idea ———— **Details** ————————————————————————

The Nucleus
Use with pages 111–114.

Describe *Rutherford's model of the atom by completing the following statements.*

1. Most of an atom consists of __electrons__ moving __rapidly__ through __empty space__.

2. The electrons are __held__ within the atom by their __attraction__ to the positively charged __nucleus__.

3. The volume of __space__ through which the electrons move is many times __larger__ than the volume of the __nucleus__.

Organize *the properties of subatomic particles by completing the table below. Use Table 4.3 for reference.*

	Electron	Proton	Neutron
Symbol	e⁻	p	n
Location	surrounding the nucleus	in nucleus	in nucleus
Relative electrical charge	1–	1+	0

Summarize *what you have learned about subatomic particles by completing the following paragraph.*

Atoms have a __spherical__ shape. The __nucleus__ of an atom is made up of __protons__ that have a positive charge and __neutrons__ that have no __charge__. The nucleus makes up __99.97%__ of the mass of an atom. Most of an __atom__ is made up of negatively charged __electrons__ traveling around the __positively__ charged nucleus. The __electrons__ are held in place by their __attraction__ to the positive charge of the __nucleus__. The __mass__ of the protons and neutrons are almost __equal__ to each other while the __mass__ of the electrons is __extremely small__.

The Structure of the Atom
Section 4.3 How Atoms Differ

(Main Idea) ——— **(Details)** ——————————————

Skim *Section 3 of your text. Focus on the headings, boldfaced words, and main ideas. Then summarize the main ideas of this section.*

1. Accept all reasonable responses.

2. _____

3. _____

New Vocabulary *In the left margin, write the term defined below.*

atomic number

the number of protons in an atom

isotope

atoms with the same number of protons but different numbers of neutrons

mass number

the sum of the number of protons and neutrons in the nucleus

atomic mass unit (amu)

1/12 the mass of a carbon-12 atom; the standard unit of measurement for the mass of atoms

atomic mass

the weighted average mass of the isotopes of an element

Academic Vocabulary *Define the following term.*

specific

characterized by precise formulation or accurate restriction

Section 4.3 How Atoms Differ (continued)

Main Idea ——— **Details** ————————————————————————

Atomic Number

Use with page 115.

Explain *how to use an atomic number to identify an element by completing the paragraph below.*

Each __atom__ of an element has a unique number of __protons__.

Since the overall charge of an atom is __neutral__ the number

of __protons__ equals the number of __electrons__. Atomic

number = number of __protons__ = number of __electrons__. If you

know how many one of the three an atom contains, you also know

the other __two__. Once you know the __atomic number__, the

__periodic table__ can be used to find the name of the __element__.

Atomic Number

Use with Example Problem 4.1, page 116.

Solve *Read Example Problem 4.1 in your text.*

You Try It

Problem –––

Given the following information about atoms, determine the name of each atom's element and its atomic number.

  a. Atom 1 has 11 protons   **b. Atom 2 has 20 electrons**

1. Analyze the Problem

Apply the relationship among atomic number, number of protons, and number of electrons to determine the name and atomic number of each element.

2. Solve for the Unknown

a. Atom 1

Atomic number = number of protons = number of electrons

Atomic number = __11__ = number of electrons

The element with an atomic number of 11 is __sodium (Na)__.

b. Atom 2

Atomic number = number of protons = number of electrons

Atomic number = number of protons = __20__

The element with an atomic number of __20__ is __calcium (Ca)__.

3. Evaluate the Answer

The answers agree with __atomic numbers__ and element

__symbols__ given in the periodic table.

Section 4.3 How Atoms Differ (continued)

⟨Main Idea⟩	⟨Details⟩

Isotopes and Mass Number

Use with page 117.

Review *your understanding of isotopes and mass number by completing the following paragraph.*

Isotopes are elements with ___the same number of protons___ but with ___differing numbers of neutrons___. The number of neutrons can be determined by ___subtracting___ the atomic number from the ___mass number___. The mass number is ___the number of protons plus neutrons in an atom___.

Use Atomic Number and Mass Number

Use with Example Problem 4.2, page 118.

Solve *Read Example Problem 4.2 in your text.*

You Try It

Problem

You are given two samples of carbon. The first sample, carbon-12, has a mass number of 12, the second sample, carbon-13, has a mass number of 13. Both samples have an atomic number of 6. Determine the number of protons, electrons, and neutrons in each sample.

1. Analyze the Problem

Known:

Carbon-12
Mass number is ___12___
Atomic number is ___6___

Carbon-13
Mass number is ___13___
Atomic number is ___6___

Unknown:

The number of protons, electrons, and neutrons in each sample.

2. Solve for the Unknown

Number of protons = number of electrons = atomic number = ___6___

Number of neutrons = mass number − atomic number

The number of neutrons for carbon-12 = 12 − 6 = ___6___

The number of neutrons for carbon-13 = 13 − 6 = ___7___

3. Evaluate the Answer

The number of neutrons does equal the ___mass number___ minus the ___atomic number___, or the number of protons.

Section 4.3 How Atoms Differ (continued)

Main Idea ——— Details ————————————————————————

Mass of Atoms

Use with pages 119–120.

Explain *why the mass number for chlorine is more than 35. Use Figure 4.17 for reference.*

Elements can have several isotopes. Each isotope has a different number of

neutrons. Therefore each isotope has a different mass. The atomic mass of an

element is a weighted average mass of all the isotopes of that element.

Calculate Atomic Mass

Use with Example Problem 4.3, page 121.

Summarize *Fill in the blanks to help you take notes while you read Example Problem 4.3.*

Problem --

Given the ___data___ in the table in the left margin, ___calculate___ the

___atomic mass___ of unknown element X. Then, ___identify___ the unknown

___element___, which is used ___medically___ to treat some ___mental disorders___.

1. **Analyze the problem**

Isotope Abundance for Element X		
Isotope	Mass (amu)	Percent abundance
^{6}X	6.015	7.59%
^{7}X	7.016	92.41%

   Known: Unknown:

   For isotope ^{6}X: ___atomic mass___ of X = ? amu

   mass = ___6.015 amu___   ___name___ of element X = ?

   abundance = ___7.59% = 0.0759___

   For isotope ^{7}X:

   mass = ___7.016 amu___

   abundance = ___92.41% = 0.9241___

2. **Solve for the unknown**

   Mass contribution = (___mass___)(___percent abundance___)

   For ^{6}X: Mass contribution = ___(6.015 amu)(0.0759)___ = ___0.4565 amu___

   For ^{7}X: Mass contribution = ___(7.016 amu)(0.9241)___ = ___6.483 amu___

   Sum the mass contributions to find the atomic mass.

   ___Atomic mass___ of X = ___(0.4565 amu + 6.483 amu)___ = ___6.939 amu___

   Use the ___periodic table___ to identify the element.

   The element with an atomic mass of 6.939 amu is ___lithium___.

3. **Evaluate the answer**

   The number of neutrons does equal the ___mass number___ minus

   the ___atomic number___, or number of ___protons___.

The Stucture of the Atom
Section 4.4 Unstable Nuclei and Radioactive Decay

Main Idea ————   **Details** ————————————————————————

Skim *Section 4 of your text. Write two questions that come to mind from reading the headings, and the captions.*

1. Accept all reasonable responses _____

2. _____

New Vocabulary   *Use your text to define each term.*

radioactivity	the process in which substances spontaneously emit radiation
radiation	rays and particles emitted by radioactive materials
nuclear reaction	a reaction in which the atom of one element changes into the atom of another element
radioactive decay	the process by which unstable nuclei lose energy by emitting radiation in a spontaneous process
alpha radiation	radiation deflected toward a negatively charged plate in a magnetic field
alpha particle	a particle with two protons and two neutrons with a 2+ charge; they are emitted during radioactive decay
nuclear equation	an equation detailing the atomic number and mass numbers of particles involved in radioactive decay
beta radiation	radiation deflected toward a positively charged plate in a magnetic field
beta particle	a fast moving electron with a 1− charge; they are emitted during radioactive decay
gamma ray	high-energy radiation that possesses no mass and is not deflected by electric or magnetic fields

Section 4.4 Unstable Nuclei and Radioactive Decay (continued)

Main Idea ———

Details ———————————————————

Radioactivity

Use with pages 122–124.

Explain *radioactivity by completing the paragraph below.*

In chemical reactions, atoms may be __rearranged__, but their

__identities__ do not change. The rearrangement __affects__

only the __electrons__ of the atoms, not the __nuclei__.

__Nuclear reactions__ are different. In nuclear reactions,

__unstable nuclei__ gain stability by emitting __radiation__. As a

result of __changes__ in the nuclei, the atoms' __identities__

change. __Unstable nuclei__ will continue emitting __radiation__,

in a process called __radioactive decay__, until stable nuclei,

often of a __different element__, are formed.

Sequence *the steps of a nuclear reaction.*

__4__ A stable, nonradioactive atom is formed.

__2__ Radiation is emitted.

__3__ The process of radioactive decay continues until the nucleus is stable.

__1__ An atom has an unstable nucleus.

Distinguish *between alpha, beta, and gamma radiation by completing the table below.*

	Radiation Type		
	Alpha	**Beta**	**Gamma**
Symbol	$^4_2 He$	β	γ
Mass (amu)	4	1/1840	0
Charge	2+	1−	0

Discuss *why some elements are radioactive while most elements are not.*

Atoms are unstable when there are too many or to few neutrons present.

They will undergo radioactive decay until the nucleus becomes

stable. Most atoms have already decayed into stable atoms.

The Structure of the Atom Chapter Wrap-Up

Now that you have read the chapter, review what you have learned. List three important things you learned about the structure of an atom.

Accept all reasonable responses.

_____

_____

_____

_____

Review

Use this checklist to help you study.

☐ Study your Science Notebook for this chapter.

☐ Study the definitions of vocabulary words.

☐ Review daily homework assignments.

☐ Reread the chapter and review the tables, graphs, and illustrations.

☐ Review the Section Assessment questions at the end of each section.

☐ Look over the Study Guide at the end of the chapter.

REAL-WORLD CONNECTION

Radioactive materials are used in power plants and for medical uses. Some people object to the widespread use of nuclear reactors and radioactive materials. Discuss how what you've learned in this chapter affects your view on the use of radioactive materials.

Accept all reasonable responses. Students should consider the nature of radioactive decay

and disposal of radioactive materials.

_____

_____

_____

Electrons in Atoms

Before You Read

Chapter 4

Review *the structure of the atom by completing the following table.*

Part of the Atom	Description
proton	**a subatomic particle with a positive charge found in the nucleus**
nucleus	centrally located part of the atom that contains protons and neutrons
electron	**negatively charged subatomic part of the atom**
neutron	subatomic particle with no charge found in the ___nucleus___

Draw *a typical atom and label the structures.*

Identify *three facts about electrons.*

Example: Electrons are a part of the structure of an atom.
Accept all reasonable responses. Possible answers include:

1. **Most of an atom consists of electrons.** _____

2. **The mass of an electron is extremely small.** _____

3. **The negative charge of an electron balances the positive charge**
   of the nucleus. _____

Electrons in Atoms
Section 5.1 Light and Quantized Energy

Main Idea —— **Details** ——————————

Scan *Section 1 of your text. Use the checklist below as a guide.*

- Read all section titles.
- Read all boldfaced words.
- Read all tables and graphs.
- Look at all pictures and read the captions.

Write three facts you discovered about light.

1. Accept all reasonable responses._____

2. _____

3. _____

New Vocabulary *Use your text to define each term.*

electromagnetic radiation	a form of energy that exhibits wavelike behavior as it travels through space
wavelength	the shortest distance between equivalent points on a continuous wave
frequency	the number of waves that pass through a given point per second
amplitude	the height of a wave from the origin to a crest or trough
electromagnetic spectrum	all forms of electromagnetic radiation
quantum	the minimum amount of energy that can be gained or lost by an atom
Planck's constant	value used to determine the energy of a quantum
photoelectric effect	phenomenon where electrons are emitted from a metal's surface when light of a certain frequency shines on the surface
photon	a particle of electromagnetic radiation with no mass that carries a quantum of energy
atomic emission spectrum	set of frequencies of electromagnetic waves emitted by atoms of an element

Section 5.1 Light and Quantized Energy (continued)

Main Idea ———— **Details**

The Atom and Unanswered Questions

Use with page 136.

Go over

List *the three reasons scientists found Rutherford's nuclear atomic model to be fundamentally incomplete.*

1. The model did not explain how the atom's electrons are arranged in the space around the nucleus.

2. It did not address the question of why the negatively charged electrons are not pulled into the atom's positively charged nucleus.

3. It did not account for the differences in chemical behavior among the various elements.

Wave Nature of Light

Use with pages 137–140.

Explain *the relationship shown by the figure below. Use the following terms: wavelength, frequency, amplitude, and speed.*

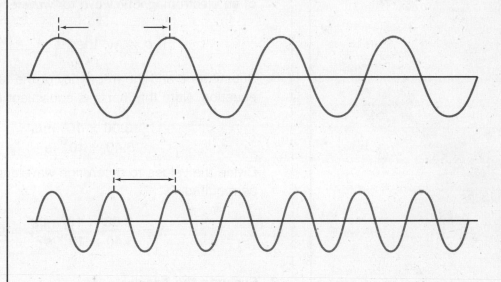

There is an inverse relationship between wavelength and frequency.

As wavelength increases, frequency decreases. Speed and

amplitude are not affected by wavelength and frequency.

Section 5.1 Light and Quantized Energy (continued)

Main Idea —————

Calculating Wavelength of an EM Wave

Use with Example Problem 5.1, page 140.

Details ————————————————

Solve *Read Example Problem 5.1 in your text.*

You Try It

Problem —·—·—·—·—·—·—·—·—·—·—·—·—·—·—·

Radio waves are used to transmit information on various channels. What is the wavelength of a radio wave having the frequency of 5.40×10^{10} Hz?

1. Analyze the Problem

Known: $v = 5.40 \times 10^{10}$ **Hz** and $c = 3.00 \times 10^8$ **m/s**

Unknown: $\lambda = ?$ **m**

You know that because radio waves are part of the electromagnetic spectrum, their speed, frequency, and wavelength are related by the formula $c = \lambda v$.

2. Solve for the Unknown

Solve the equation relating the speed, frequency, and wavelength of an electromagnetic wave for wavelength (λ).

If $c = \lambda v$, then $\lambda = $ __*c/v*__

Substitute c and the frequency of the radio wave, v, into the equation. Note that hertz is equivalent to $1/s$ or s^{-1}.

$$\lambda = \frac{3.00 \times 10^8 \text{ m/s}}{5.40 \times 10^{10} \text{ s}^{-1}}$$

Divide the values to determine wavelength, λ, and cancel units as required.

$$\lambda = \frac{3.00 \times 10^8 \text{ m/s}}{5.40 \times 10^{10} \text{ s}^{-1}} = 0.555 \times 10^{-2} \text{ m}$$

3. Evaluate the Answer

The answer is correctly expressed in a unit of __wavelength (m)__ .

Both of the known values in the problem are expressed with __3__ significant figures, so the answer must have __3__ significant figures.

Section 5.1 Light and Quantized Energy (continued)

Main Idea ——— **Details** ———————————————

Particle Nature of Light

Use with pages 141–143.

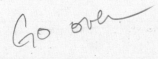

Go over

Go over after all slides

Identify *two facts the wave model of light failed to explain.*

1. Heated objects emit only certain frequencies of light at a given temperature.

2. Some metals emit electrons when colored light of a specific frequency shines on them. *See slide*

Describe *Planck's quantum concept by completing the following statement.*

The quantum concept concludes that matter can gain or lose _____energy_____ only in small, specific amounts called _____quanta_____.
A quantum is the minimum amount of energy that can be _____gained_____ or _____lost_____ by an atom.

Atomic Emission Spectra

Use with pages 144–145.

Compare and contrast *Einstein's equation with Planck's equation by completing the following sentence.*

Planck's equation, $E_{quantum} = h\nu$, demonstrates mathematically that the energy of a quantum is related to the _____frequency_____ of the emitted radiation. Einstein went further by explaining that, in addition to its wavelike characteristics, a beam of light can be thought of as a stream of _tiny particles_ called _____photons_____.

Contrast *the continuous electromagnetic spectra and the atomic emission spectra.*

The electromagnetic spectrum is a *continuous* spectrum of colors

because there is no portion of it that does not correspond to a

unique wavelength and frequency of light. The atomic emission

spectrum, also known as a line spectrum, consists of *distinct*

colored lines of different frequencies.

Electrons in Atoms

Section 5.2 Quantum Theory and the Atom

Main Idea	Details
	Skim *Section 2 of your text. Write three questions that come to mind from reading the headings and the illustration captions.*
	1. Accept all reasonable answers.
	2.
	3.

New Vocabulary   *Use your text to define each term.*

ground state	the lowest allowable energy state of an atom
quantum number	number assigned to each orbit of an electron
de Broglie equation	equation that predicts that all moving particles have wave characteristics
Heisenberg uncertainty principle	states that both the velocity and position of a particle cannot be known at the same time
quantum mechanical model of the atom	the atomic model in which electrons are treated as waves
atom orbital	a three-dimensional region around the nucleus
principal quantum number	number indicating the relative sizes and energies of atomic orbitals
principal energy level	major energy levels of an atom
energy sublevel	an energy level contained within a principal energy level

Section 5.2 Quantum Theory and the Atom (continued)

Main Idea ——— **Details** ———————————————————

Bohr Model of the Atom

Use with pages 146–148.

Classify *the characteristics of each series in hydrogen's line spectrum. Include the following information.*

1. Beginning orbit(s)/ending orbit
2. Description of the spectral lines

Balmer	Paschen	Lyman
1. electrons drop from the third, fourth, fifth, and sixth orbits to the second orbit	1. electrons drop from the fourth, fifth, sixth, and seventh orbits to first to the third orbit	1. electrons drop from all higher orbits to the first orbit
2. four distinct colors	2. infrared	2. ultraviolet

The Quantum Mechanical Model of the Atom

Use with pages 149–150

Sequence *de Broglie's process in developing his equation by completing the flow chart below.*

Whole __numbers__ of __wavelengths__ are allowed in a circular orbit of fixed __radius__.

Light has both __wave__ and __particle__ characteristics.

Can particles of matter, including electrons, behave like __waves__?

If an electron has __wavelike motion__ and is restricted to circular orbits of fixed radius, the __electron__ is allowed only certain possible wavelengths, __frequencies__, and __energies__.

Section 5.2 Quantum Theory and the Atom (continued)

⟨Main Idea⟩ ——— **⟨Details⟩** ——————————————

The Heisenberg Uncertainty Principle

Use with pages 151–152.

Discuss *how Heisenberg's principle influenced Schrödinger to develop his wave equation.*

Heisenberg's uncertainty principle states that it is impossible to know both the velocity and position of a particle at the same time.

This insight allowed Schrödinger to develop an equation for finding the probable location of an electron rather than a specific location.

The probable location of the electrons is called the atomic orbital.

Hydrogen's Atomic Orbitals

Use with page 153.

Identify *four facts about atomic orbitals by completing the following statements.*

1. ____Principal quantum numbers____ indicate the relative sizes and energies of atomic orbitals.

2. The atom's major energy levels are called ____principal energy levels____.

3. Principal energy levels contain ____sublevels____.

4. The number of ____energy sublevels____ in a principal energy level ____increases____ as n increases.

SUMMARIZE Compare and contrast the Bohr and quantum mechanical models of the atom.

Both consider ground state of the atom to be when the electron is in the n = 1 orbit. Bohr

believed that atoms moved around the nucleus in certain allowed circular orbits, whereas the

quantum model suggests a three-dimensional region around the nucleus called an atomic

orbital. The quantum theory further accounts for the chemical behavior of atoms and applies

to hydrogen as well as other elements. Bohr's theory only explained the spectrum of

hydrogen.

Electrons in Atoms
Section 5.3 Electron Configuration

(Main Idea) ——   (Details) —————————————————————

Skim *Section 3 of your text. Focus on the headings, subheadings, boldfaced words, and figure captions. Summarize the main ideas of this section.*

Accept all reasonable responses._____

_____

_____

_____

(New Vocabulary)   *Use your text to define each term.*

electron configuration   the arrangement of electrons in an atom_____

aufbau principle   states that electrons occupy the lowest energy orbital available

Pauli exclusion principle   states that only two electrons may share an atomic orbital, and only

when they have opposite spins_____

Hund's rule   states that single electrons with the same spin must occupy each

equal-energy orbital before additional electrons with opposite spins

can enter the same orbitals_____

valence electron   electrons in the atom's outermost orbital_____

electron-dot structure   structure consisting of the element's symbol, which represents the

atomic nucleus and inner-level electrons, surrounded by dots

representing the atom's valence electrons_____

Section 5.3 Electron Configurations (continued)

Main Idea	Details

Ground-State Electron Configurations

Use with page 156.

Organize *information about electron configurations by completing the following outline.*

Electron configuration is __the arrangement of electrons in an atom__.

I. Ground–state electron configurations

    A. Three rules define how electrons can be arranged in an atom's orbitals:

        1. __The aufbau principle__

        2. __The Pauli exclusion principle__

        3. __Hund's rule__

Orbital Diagrams and Electron Configuration Notation

Use with page 158.

    B. The _____two_____ methods for representing an atom's electron configuration

        1. Orbital diagrams

            a. An empty box represents an __unoccupied orbital__.

            b. A box containing a single up arrow represents an orbital with __one electron__.

            c. A box containing both up and down arrows represents a __filled orbital__.

            d. Each box is labeled with the __principal quantum number__ and __sublevel__ associated with the orbital.

        2. __Electron configuration notations__

            a. This method designates the __principal energy level__ and __energy sublevel__ associated with each of the atom's orbitals, and includes a __superscript representing the number of electrons in the orbital__

Valence Electrons

Use with page 161.

    C. Only valence electrons __determine the chemical properties of an element__.

        1. Electron-dot structures consist of the __element's symbol__, which represents the __atomic nucleus and inner-level electrons__, surrounded by dots representing the __atom's valence electrons__.

Section 5.3 Electron Configurations (continued)

Main Idea	Details
Electron-Dot Structures	**Solve** *Read Example Problem 5.3 in your text.*

Electron-Dot Structures

Use with Example Problem 5.3, page 162.

Solve *Read Example Problem 5.3 in your text.*

You Try It
Problem --•

Ruthenium (Ru) is commonly used in the manufacture of platinum alloys. What is the ground-state electron configuration for an atom of ruthenium?

1. Analyze the Problem

Known: the element ruthenium

Unknown: the ground-state electron configuration

Determine the number of additional electrons a ruthenium atom has compared to the nearest preceding noble gas, and then write out ruthenium's electron configuration.

2. Solve for the Unknown

From the periodic table, ruthenium's atomic number is determined to be 44 . Thus a ruthenium atom contains 44 electrons. The noble gas preceding ruthenium is krypton (Kr), which has an atomic number of 36. Represent ruthenium's first 36 electrons using the chemical symbol for krypton written inside brackets.

____[Kr]____

The first 36 electrons have filled out the 1s, 2s, 2p, 3s, 3p, 4s, 3d and 4p sublevels. The remaining 8 electrons of ruthenium's configuration need to be written out. Thus, the remaining 8 electrons fill the __5s and 4d__ orbitals.

Using the maximum number of electrons that can fill each orbital, write out the electron configuration. __[Kr] $5s^2 4d^3$__

3. Evaluate the Answer

All 44 electrons in a ruthenium atom have been accounted for. The correct preceding noble gas ____[Kr]____ has been used in the notation, and the order of orbital filling for the __fifth period__ is correct.

Electrons in Atoms Chapter Wrap-Up

Review

Now that you have read the chapter, review what you have learned. Write out the key equations and relationships.
Possible answers:

$c = \lambda v$ **The speed of light is the product of its wavelength (λ)**

and its frequency (v).

$E_{quantum} = hv$

$\lambda = \dfrac{h}{mv}$

Key relationships:
Wavelength/frequency
The wave nature of light/the particle nature of light
The Bohr model of the atom/the quantum mechanical model of the atom

Use this checklist to help you study.

☐ Study your Science Notebook for this chapter.

☐ Study the definitions for vocabulary words.

☐ Review daily homework assignments.

☐ Reread the chapter and review the tables, graphs, and illustrations.

☐ Review the Section Assessment questions at the end of each section.

☐ Look over the Study Guide at the end of the chapter.

REAL-WORLD CONNECTION

Explain how advances in our understanding of the atom influence our daily lives.

Accept all reasonable responses. Possible answer: Advances influence our daily lives

through the use of medical procedures such as laser surgery, through industrial technology

using radiography, cell phones, broader bands for television and radio, and more.

_____

_____

The Periodic Table and Periodic Law

Before You Read

Review Vocabulary) **Define** *the following terms.*

atom
| the smallest particle of an element that retains the properties of that element |

electron configuration
| the arrangement of electrons in an atom |

valence electrons
| electrons in an atom's outermost orbit |

electron-dot structure
| consists of an element's symbol, representing the atomic nucleus and inner-level electrons, that is surrounded by dots, representing the atom's valance electrons |

Chapter 4

Distinguish *between the subatomic particles in terms of relative charge.*

Subatomic Particle	Electrical Charge
proton	positive
electron	negative
neutron	neutral

Describe *how the subatomic particles are arranged.*

The center of the atom is made of a nucleus which contains the protons and neutrons. Electrons are located in the space around the nucleus.

The Periodic Table and Periodic Law
Section 6.1 Development of the Modern Periodic Table

Main Idea ————

Details ——————————————————————

Skim *Section 1 of your text. Look at the headings, boldfaced words, figures and captions. Write two facts you discovered about the periodic table.*

1. Accept all reasonable responses.

2. _____

New Vocabulary *Use your text to define each term.*

periodic law the statement that there is a periodic repetition of chemical and physical properties of elements when arranged by increasing atomic number

group vertical columns of elements arranged in order of increasing atomic number on the periodic table

period horizontal rows of elements arranged in order of increasing atomic number on the periodic table

representative element elements in groups 1, 2, and 13-18 in the periodic table

transition element elements in groups 3-12 in the periodic table

metal one of the three main classifications of the periodic table

alkali metal group 1 elements, except hydrogen

alkaline earth metal group 2 elements

transition metal elements in groups 3-12, except lanthanide and actinide elements

inner transition metal lanthanide and actinide series of elements

nonmetal a gas or dull, brittle solids that are poor conductors of heat and electricity

halogen a highly reactive group 17 element

noble gas extremely unreactive group 18 element

metalloid has properties of both metals and nonmetals

Name_____ Date _____

Section 6.1 Development of the Modern Periodic Table (continued)

Main Idea	Details

Development of the Periodic Table

Use with pages 174–176.

Sequence *the events that helped develop the periodic table.*

1. In the 1790's, _Antoine Lavoisier compiled a list of 33 known elements_.

2. In 1864, _John Newlands arranged elements by increasing atomic mass_ and saw the properties of elements _repeated every eighth element_.

3. In 1869, _Mendeleev arranged elements by increasing atomic mass into columns with similar properties_. He left blank spaces _for undiscovered elements_.

4. In 1913, _Moseley discovered that each element has a unique number of protons equal to its atomic number_. He arranged elements by _atomic number instead of atomic mass_.

The Modern Periodic Table

Use with pages 177–180.

Determine *where you can find each of the following groups of elements on the periodic table below:*

alkali metals   nonmetals   halogens

alkaline earth metals representative elements   transition metals

inner transition metals transition elements   noble gases

Hint: colored pencils might be helpful. Be sure to include a legend.

PERIODIC TABLE OF THE ELEMENTS

Student responses should be similar to Figure 6.7.

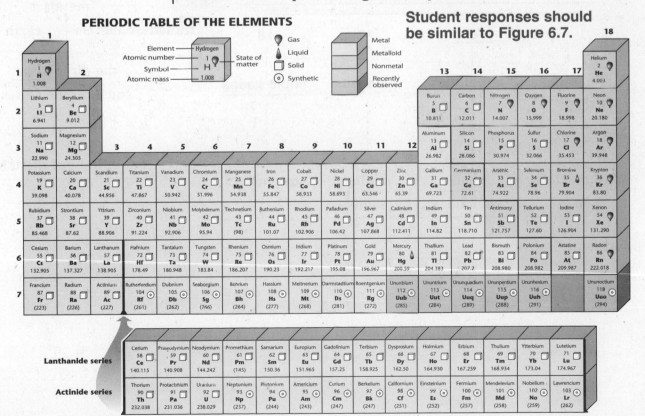

Section 6.1 Development of the Modern Periodic Table (continued)

Main Idea ——— **Details** ———————————————————

Organize *information about the periodic table by completing the concept map below.*

The periodic table has <u>seven</u> rows called periods.

The table has <u>18</u> columns called

<u>groups</u> or families

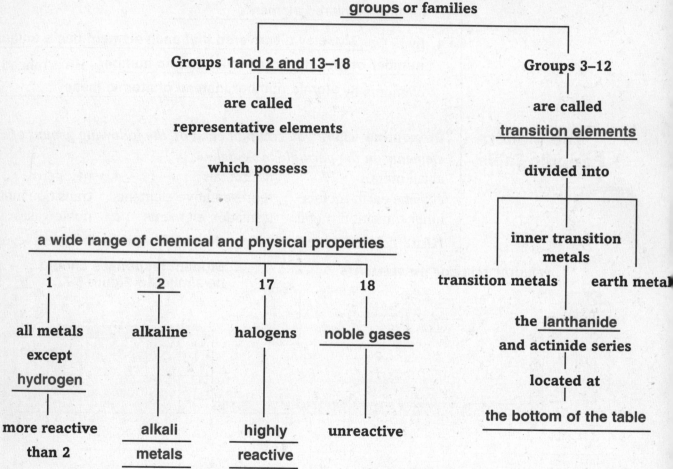

Groups 1 and <u>2 and 13–18</u>

are called

<u>representative elements</u>

which possess

<u>a wide range of chemical and physical properties</u>

| 1 | 2 | 17 | 18 |

<u>all metals except hydrogen</u>

<u>alkaline</u>

<u>halogens</u>

<u>noble gases</u>

more reactive than 2

<u>alkali metals</u>

<u>highly reactive</u>

unreactive

Groups 3–12

are called

<u>transition elements</u>

divided into

inner transition metals

transition metals   earth metal

the <u>lanthanide</u> and actinide series

located at

<u>the bottom of the table</u>

Section 6.1 Development of the Modern Periodic Table (continued)

Main Idea ——— **Details** —————————————————————————————

Identify *the information that is given on a typical box from the periodic table.*

1. element name _____

2. symbol _____

3. atomic number _____

4. atomic mass _____

5. state of matter _____

Match *the box color on the periodic table in Figure 6.5 with the class of element the box describes.*

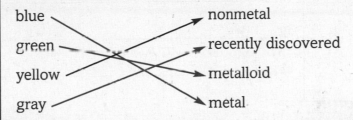

blue   nonmetal

green   recently discovered

yellow   metalloid

gray   metal

REAL-WORLD CONNECTION Describe how knowledge of the periodic table would be important in three different careers, based on what you've read.

Accept all reasonable responses. Possible answers include: chemists use the periodic table

to predict the behavior of elements; engineers use the periodic table to create new materials

used in high-tech applications; research scientists use the periodic table to predict the

behavior of atoms in experiments; and science teachers use the periodic table to help

students learn chemistry.

The Periodic Table and Periodic Law
Section 6.2 Classification of the Elements

Main Idea ————— **Details** —————————————————

Scan *Section 2 of your text. Use the checklist below as a guide.*

• Read all section titles.

• Read all boldfaced words.

• Read all tables.

• Look at all pictures and read the captions.

• Think about what you already know about the shapes and arrangements of atoms in covalent compounds.

Write *three facts that you discovered about the relationship between electrons and an element's location on the periodic table.*

1. Accept all reasonable responses. _____

2. _____

3. _____

Academic Vocabulary *Define the following terms.*

structure something made up of more-or-less interdependent elements or parts _____

Section 6.2 Classification of the Elements (continued)

⟨ **Main Idea** ⟩ ——— ⟨ **Details** ⟩ ———————————————

Organizing the Elements by Electron Configuration

Use with pages 182–183.

Organize *information about electron configurations by completing the outline below.*

I. Electrons

    A. Valence electrons

        1. electrons in __the highest principal energy level of an atom__

        2. atoms in the __same group__ have __the same number of valence electrons__.

    B. Valence electrons and period

        1. The __energy level__ of an element's valence electrons indicates __the period on the periodic table in which it is found__.

            a. Elements with valence electrons in energy level 2 are found in __the second period__.

            b. Elements with __valence electrons in energy level 4__ are found in the fourth period.

    C. Valence electrons and group number

        1. Representative elements.

            a. All elements in group 1 have __one valence electron__.

            b. All elements in group 2 have __two valence electrons__.

            c. Group 13 elements have __three valence electrons__, group 14 elements have __four valence electrons__ and so on.

        2. Helium, in group 18, is an __exception__.

Describe *the relationship between the number of valence electrons and the chemical properties of atoms.*

__Atoms in the same group have similar chemical properties because__

__they have the same number of valence electrons.__

_____

Section 6.2 Classification of the Elements (continued)

Main Idea —— **Details** ——————————————

The s-, p-, d-, and f-Block Elements

Use with pages 183–185.

Distinguish *between s-, p-, d-, and f-block elements by completing the table below.*

	Periodic Table Groups	Orbitals	Type of Occupied Element
s-block	1 and 2	s	representative elements
p-block	13 through 18	p	**representative elements**
d-block	3 through 12	s and d	transition metals
f-block	lanthanide and actinide series	s, 4f, and 5f	inner transition metals

Electron Configuration and the Periodic Table

Use with Example Problem 6.1, page 186.

Summarize *Fill in the blanks to help you take notes while you read Example Problem 6.1.*

Problem -–-–-–-–-–-–-–-–-–-–-–-–-–-–-–-

Without using the periodic table, determine the group, period, and block in which strontium is located on the periodic table.

1. **Analyze the problem**

   Known: Unknown:

   $[Kr]5s^2$ **location on the periodic table**

   Use the electron configuration of strontium to determine its place.

2. **Solve for the unknown**

   Group: Strontium has a valence configuration of $\underline{s^2}$. All group
   $\underline{2}$ elements have the $\underline{s^2}$ configuration.

   Period: The $\underline{5}$ in $5s^2$ indicates that strontium is in **period 5**.

   Block: The $\underline{s^2}$ indicates that strontium's valence electrons
   $\underline{\text{fill the s sublevel}}$. Therefore, strontium is in the $\underline{\text{s-block}}$.

3. **Evaluate the answer**

   The relationships among $\underline{\text{electron configuration}}$ and
   $\underline{\text{position on the periodic table}}$ have been correctly applied.

The Periodic Table and Periodic Law

Section 6.3 Periodic Trends

(Main Idea) ———— **(Details)** ————————————————

Scan *Section 3 of your text. Use the checklist below as a guide.*

• Read all section titles.

• Read all boldfaced words.

• Read all tables.

• Look at all pictures and read the captions.

Write *three facts that you discovered about periodic trends.*

1. Accept all reasonable responses. _____

2. _____

3. _____

(New Vocabulary) *Use your text to define each term.*

ion	an atom or bonded group of atoms that has a positive or negative charge
ionization energy	the energy required to remove an electron from a gaseous atom
octet rule	states that atoms tend to gain, lose, or share electrons in order to acquire a full set of eight valence electrons
electronegativity	relative ability of atoms to attract electrons in a chemical bond

Section 6.3 Periodic Trends (continued)

Main Idea ———— **Details** ——————————————————

Atomic Radius

Use with pages 187–188.

Describe *how atomic size is defined.*

Atomic size is defined by how closely an atom lies to a neighboring

atom. Because the nature of the neighboring atom can vary, the size

of the atom itself also tends to vary somewhat.

Analyze *any trends that you observe in Figure 6.11 and how the trends relate to atomic mass.*

Atomic radii decreases as you move left-to-right across a period. The atomic

mass increases left to right. Atomic radii increases as you move down a

group. The atomic mass also increases as you move down the group.

Interpret Trends in Atomic Radii

Use with Example Problem 6.2, page 189.

Summarize *Fill in the blanks to help you take notes while you read Example Problem 6.2.*

Problem --

Which has the largest atomic radius: carbon (C), fluorine (F), beryllium (Be), or lithium (Li)? Explain your answer in terms of trends in atomic radii.

1. **Analyze the problem**
   Known: periodic table information for four elements

   Unknown: which of the four has the __largest atomic radius__

2. **Solve for the unknown**

   Use the __periodic table__ to determine if the elements are in the

   same group or period. All four elements are in ___period 2___.

   Order the elements from ___left-to-right___ across the period.

   lithium, beryllium, carbon, fluorine

   Determine the largest based on trends of ___atomic radii___.

   Lithium is first in period and therefore largest.

3. **Evaluate the answer**

   The __group trends__ in atomic radii have been correctly applied.

Section 6.3 Periodic Trends (continued)

Main Idea ———— **Details** ———————————————————

Ionic Radius

Use with pages 189–190.

Describe *atomic size and ionic change by completing the table below.*

Ionic Change	Ion Charge	Size of Atom
atom **loses** electrons	becomes positive	**decreases**
atom gains electrons	becomes **negative**	increases

Identify *two reasons why the relative size of an atom becomes smaller due to the loss of electrons:*

1. The atom may lose its valence electron, leaving an empty outer orbital.

2. Electrostatic repulsion among the remaining electrons decreases,

and they are pulled closer to the nucleus.

Explain *why atoms increase in size when the atom gains electrons.*

The addition of electrons increases the electrostatic repulsion,

forcing the electrons farther apart.

Ionization Energy

Use with pages 191–193.

Describe *ionization energy trends on the periodic table by completing the paragraphs below.*

Ionization energies generally __increase__ as you move left-to-right across a __period__. Increased nuclear charge leads to an __increased hold__ on valance electrons. Ionization energy generally __decreases__ when you move down a __group__. Less energy is required to remove __valence electrons__ because they are __farther__ from the nucleus.

The octet rule states that atoms tend to gain, lose, or share

__electrons__ in order to acquire a full set of __eight valence electrons__.

First period elements are the __exception__ to this rule.

Electronegativity

Use with page 194.

Predict *what part of the periodic table has the greatest electronegativity. Use Figure 6.18 for reference.*

the upper right of the table

The Periodic Table and Periodic Law Chapter Wrap-Up

Now that you have read the chapter, review what you have learned. List three facts about the periodic table and periodic law.

Accept all reasonable responses.

_____

_____

_____

_____

_____

Review

Use this check list to help you study.

☐ Study your Science Notebook for this chapter.

☐ Study the definitions and vocabulary words.

☐ Review daily homework assignments.

☐ Reread the chapter and review the tables, graphs, and illustrations.

☐ Review the Section Assessment questions at the end of each section.

☐ Look over the Study Guide at the end of the chapter.

REAL-WORLD CONNECTION

Explain how an understanding of the periodic table can help you gain confidence in studying chemistry.

Accept all reasonable responses.

_____

_____

_____

_____

Ionic Compounds and Metals

Before You Read

Define the following terms.

ion | an atom or bonded group of atoms with a positive or negative charge

ionization energy | the energy required to remove an electron from a gaseous atom;

generally increases in moving from left-to-right across a period and

decreases in moving down a group

noble gas | an extremely unreactive group 18 element

valance electron | the electrons in an atom's outermost orbitals; determine the chemical

properties of an element

Chapter 5 | **Create** *electron-dot diagrams for the following elements.*

aluminum _____Al·_____

calcium: _____·Ca·_____

arsenic: _____·As·_____

tellurium: _____:Te·_____

xenon: _____:Xe:_____

Ionic Compounds and Metals

Section 7.1 Ion Formation

———— (Details) —————————————————————————————

Skim *Section 1 of your text. Read the title and subheads. List three concepts that you think will be discussed in this section.*

1. Accept all reasonable responses. _____

2. _____

3. _____

(New **Vocabulary**) *Use your text to define each term.*

chemical bond the force that holds two atoms together _____

cation a positively charged ion; formed when one or more electrons are

removed from an atom _____

anion a negatively charged ion; formed when one or more electrons are

added to an atom _____

Name _____ **Date** _____

Section 7.1 Ion Formation (continued)

⟨ **Main Idea** ⟩———— ⟨ **Details** ⟩—————————————————

Valence Electrons and Chemical Bonds

Use with pages 206–209.

Organize *information about forming chemical bonds by completing the concept map below.*

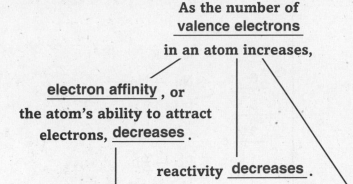

As the number of
<u>valence electrons</u>
in an atom increases,

<u>electron affinity</u> , or
the atom's ability to attract
electrons, <u>decreases</u> .

reactivity <u>decreases</u> .

Electron affinity is smallest for
<u>noble gases</u> ,
which in general have eight
<u>electrons</u> in their outermost
s and p orbitals.

<u>ionization energy</u> , which
is the energy needed to
remove electrons from
the outer orbitals,
<u>increases</u> .

Write *the electron configuration of the most likely ion and the charge that is lost or gained by each of the following atoms. Indicate what the overall charge of the ion is, and whether it is a cation or an anion.*

Cs: [Xe]$6s^1$

Cs^+: [Xe] + 1e^-
overall ion charge = +1 (cation)

O: [He]$2s^22p^4$

O^{2-}: [He]$2s^22p^6$ (or [Ne]) – 2e^-
overall ion charge = –2 (anion)

Ga: [Ar]$4s^23d^{10}4p^1$

Ga^{3+}: [Ar]$3d^{10}$ + 3e^-
overall ion charge = +3 (cation)

Br: [Ar]$4s^23d^{10}4p^5$

Br^-: [Ar]$4s^23d^{10}4p^6$ (or [Kr]) – 1e^-
overall ion charge = –1 (anion)

Ag: [Kr]$5s^14d^{10}$

Ag+: [Kr]$4d^{10}$ + 1e^-
overall ion charge = +1 (cation)

Sc: [Ar]$4s^23d^1$

Sc^{3+}: [Ar] + 3e^-
overall ion charge = +3 (cation)

Section 7.1 Ion Formation (continued)

$\boxed{\text{Main Idea}}$——— $\boxed{\text{Details}}$————————————————

Sequence *the first group of elements in order of increasing ionization energy. Sequence the second group of elements in order of increasing electron affinity.*

First Group		Second Group	
2	$K \rightarrow K^+$	**3**	$P \rightarrow P^{3-}$
6	$Ne \rightarrow Ne^+$	**2**	$O \rightarrow O^{2-}$
5	$P \rightarrow P^{5+}$	**6**	$Xe \rightarrow Xe^-$
3	$Fe \rightarrow Fe^{2+}$	**4**	$S \rightarrow S^{2-}$
1	$Rb \rightarrow Rb^+$	**5**	$I \rightarrow I^-$
4	$Mg \rightarrow Mg^{2+}$	**1**	$F \rightarrow F^-$

Identify *the following ions.*

Ag^+	**silver**
Li^+	**lithium**
Br^-	**bromide**
Ca^{2+}	**calcium**
S^{2-}	**sulfide**
B^{3+}	**boron**
As^{3-}	**arsenide**
H^-	**hydride**
Cd^{2+}	**cadmium**
Se^{2-}	**selenide**

Ionic Compounds and Metals
Section 7.2 Ionic Bonds and Ionic Compounds

Main Idea ———

Details —————————————————————

Skim *Section 2 of your text. Write three questions that come to mind from reading the headings and the illustration captions.*

1. Accept all reasonable responses._____

2. _____

3. _____

New Vocabulary   *Use your text to define each term.*

ionic bond   the electrostatic force that holds oppositely charged particles

together in an ionic compound

ionic compound   a compound that contains ionic bonds

crystal lattice   a three-dimensional geometric arrangement of particles

electrolyte   an ionic compound whose aqueous solution conducts an

electric current

lattice energy   the energy required to separate one mole of the ions of an ionic

compound

Section 7.2 Ionic Bonds and Ionic Compounds (continued)

Main Idea ———— **Details** ————————————

Formation of an Ionic Bond

Use with pages 210–212.

Solve *Read pages 211–213 in your text.*

You Try It

Problem --•

Describe the formation of an ionic compound from the elements boron and selenium.

1. Analyze the Problem

Known: the electron configurations of the given elements

$$B \rightarrow [He]2s^2 2p^1$$
$$Se \rightarrow [Ar]4s^2 3d^{10} 4p^4$$

Unknown: the number of valence electrons for each neutral atom

B → 3 valence electrons

Se → 6 valence electrons

2. Solve for the Unknown

Determine how many electrons need to be removed from boron and how many electrons need to be added to selenium to form noble gas configurations.

B has a noble gas configuration of [He] when 3 electrons are

removed. Se has a noble gas configuration of [Kr] when 2

electrons are added.

Determine how many boron atoms and how many selenium atoms must be present for the total number of electrons exchanged between the two elements to be equal.

The number 6 is the smallest number divisible by both 2 and 3.

Therefore, 2 B atoms will provide 6 electrons, which will be added

to 3 Se atoms to form the proper number of stable ions.

3. Evaluate the Answer

The overall charge on one unit of this compound is zero.

$\boxed{2}$ boron ions (3+/boron ion) + $\boxed{3}$ selenide ions ($\boxed{2-}$/

selenide ion) = $\boxed{2}$ (3+) + $\boxed{3}$ ($\boxed{2-}$) = 0

Section 7.2 Ionic Bonds and Ionic Compounds (continued)

<table>
<tr><td>

Main Idea

</td><td>

Details

</td></tr>
<tr><td>

Properties of Ionic Compounds

Use with pages 212–217.

</td><td>

Analyze *the relationship between the lattice energy of an ionic compound and the force of attraction.*

Lattice energy is a measure of the energy required to separate one

mole of the ions of an ionic compound. The more negative the

lattice energy, the stronger the force of attraction.

Describe *the relationship between the size of the ions in a compound and the compound's lattice energy.*

The smaller the ions, the more negative their lattice energy, because

the nucleus is closer to and thus has more attraction for the valence

electrons.

Explain *the relationship between lattice energy and the charge of the ion.*

The larger the positive or negative charges of ions, the more

negative their lattice energy.

Organize *the following ionic compounds from those with the least negative lattice energy to those with the most negative lattice energy.*

5	$LiCl$
8	BeS
4	$LiBr$
9	BeO
7	$BeCl_2$
3	$RbBr$
1	CsI
6	$SrCl_2$
2	$CsBr$

</td></tr>
</table>

Ionic Compounds and Metals

Section 7.3 Names and Formulas for Ionic Compounds

Main Idea ──── **Details** ──────────────────────

Scan *Section 3 of your text. Use the checklist below as a guide.*

- Read all section titles.
- Read all boldfaced words.
- Read all tables and diagrams.
- Look at all figures and read the captions.
- Study the example problems and note what they are intended to solve.
- Think about what you already know about the formation, formulas, and naming of ions and ionic compounds.

Write *three facts that you discovered about the names and formulas of ionic compounds.*

1. Accept all reasonable responses.

2. _____

3. _____

New Vocabulary *Use your text to define each term.*

formula unit | the simplest ratio of the ions represented in an ionic compound

monatomic ion | a one-atom ion

oxidation number | the charge of a monatomic ion

polyatomic ion | ions made up of more than one atom

oxyanion | a polyatomic ion composed of an element, usually a nonmetal,

bonded to one or more oxygen atoms

Academic Vocabulary *Define the following term.*

transfer | to cause to pass from one to another

Section 7.3 Names and Formulas for Ionic Compounds (continued)

Main Idea	Details

Formula for an Ionic Compound

Use with Example Problem 7.1, page 220.

Solve *Read Example Problem 7.1 in your text.*

You Try It

Problem

Calcium can form a cation with a 2+ charge. Write the formula for the ionic compound formed from calcium ion and Chlorine.

1. Analyze the Problem

Known: the ionic forms of the component elements

Ca^{2+} and Cl^{1-}

Unknown: **the compound formed from the two ions**

2. Solve for the Unknown

The smallest number that is divisible by both ionic charges is **two**, so the compound contains **one** calcium ion(s) and **two** sulfide ion(s). The formula for the ionic compound formed is **$CaCl_2$**.

3. Evaluate the Answer

The overall charge on one formula unit of this compound is zero.

$\boxed{1}$ Ca ion(s) (2+/Ca ion) + $\boxed{2}$ Cl ions (1− /Cl ion) = 0

Formula for a Polyatomic Ionic Compound

Use with Example Problem 7.3, page 222.

Solve *Read Example Problem 7.3 in your text.*

You Try It

Problem

Write the formula for the ionic compound formed from the calcium ion and the bromate ion.

1. Analyze the Problem

Known: the ionic forms of the component elements Ca^{2+}

and BrO_3^-

Unknown: **the compound formed from the two ions**

Section 7.3 Names and Formulas for Ionic Compounds (continued)

Main Idea ———— **Details** —————————————————————

2. **Solve for the Unknown**

   The smallest number that is divisible by both ionic charges is __two__, so __two__ bromate ions combine with __one__ calcium ion. The formula for the ionic compound formed is to form __$Ca(BrO_3)_2$__.

3. **Evaluate the Answer**

   The overall charge on one formula unit of this compound is zero.

   1 Ca ion (2+/Ca ion) + [2] BrO_3 ions (1−/BrO_3 ion) = 0

Names for Ions and Ionic Compounds

Use with pages 222–224.

Classify *the ions listed below as monatomic or polyatomic cations or anions. If the ion is a polyatomic anion, indicate whether it is an oxyanion.*

CN^-	polyatomic anion
MnO_4^-	polyatomic anion, oxyanion
Ba^{2+}	monatomic cation
$Fe(CN)_6^{4-}$	polyatomic anion
NH_4^+	polyatomic cation
N^{3-}	monatomic anion
Hg_2^{2+}	polyatomic cation
$S_2O_3^{2-}$	polyatomic anion, oxyanion
O^{2-}	monatomic anion

Identify *the ionic compounds listed below.*

CaO	calcium oxide
$KMnO_4$	potassium permanganate
$Sr(IO_3)_2$	strontium iodate
NH_4OH	ammonium hydroxide
Fe_2S_3	iron (III) sulfide
$Sn(NO_3)_4$	tin (IV) nitrate
$Pb_3(PO_4)_2$	lead (II) phosphate
Hg_2SO_4	mercury (I) sulfate
$PtCl_4$	platinum (IV) chloride

Ionic Compounds and Metals

Section 7.4 Metallic Bonds and the Properties of Metals

Main Idea ── Details ──────────────────────────

Skim *Section 4 of your text. Write three questions that come to mind from reading the headings and the illustration captions.*

1. Accept all reasonable responses._____

2. _____

3. _____

New Vocabulary   *Use your text to define each term.*

electron sea model   model in which all metal atoms in a metallic solid contribute their

valence electrons to form a "sea" of electrons, which can move

freely between atoms in the metal

delocalized electrons   electrons present in the outer energy levels of the bonding metallic

atoms that are free to move between atoms because they are not

held by any specific atom

metallic bond   the attraction of a metallic cation for delocalized electrons

alloy   a mixture of elements that has metallic properties

Section 7.4 Metallic Bonds and the Properties of Metals (continued)

Main Idea	Details

Metallic Bonds

Use with pages 225–226.

Summarize *how the electron sea model accounts for the malleability, high thermal conductivity, and high electrical conductivity of metals.*

An applied force causes metal ions to move through delocalized

electrons in the "electron sea," making metals malleable and

ductile. The movement of delocalized electrons around positive

metallic cations carries heat and electrical energy throughout

the metal.

Explain *the properties of metals by completing the following sentences.*

The __strength and hardness__ of transition metals increases as the

number of delocalized electrons __increases__ .

Because the __cations__ in metals are strongly attracted to the

delocalized electrons in the metal, they are not easily __removed__

from the metal, causing the metal to be very __durable__ .

Alkali metals are __softer__ than transition metals because they have

only __one delocalized electron__ per atom.

The __melting points__ of metals vary greatly. The melting points

are not as extreme as the __boiling points__ . It does not take an

extreme amount of energy for __atoms of a metal__ to be able to

move past each other. However, during __boiling__ , atoms must be

separated from a group of __cations and electrons__ , which

requires a lot of __energy__ .

Light absorbed and released by the __delocalized electrons__ in a

metal accounts for the __luster__ of the metal.

Section 7.4 Metallic Bonds and the Properties of Metals (continued)

Main Idea ———— **Details** ————————————————————

Metal Alloys

Use with pages 227–228.

Match *the alloy composition given in the first column with the common name of the alloy in the second column and the alloy's uses in the third column. Draw lines between the appropriate items. Use Table 7.13 as a reference.*

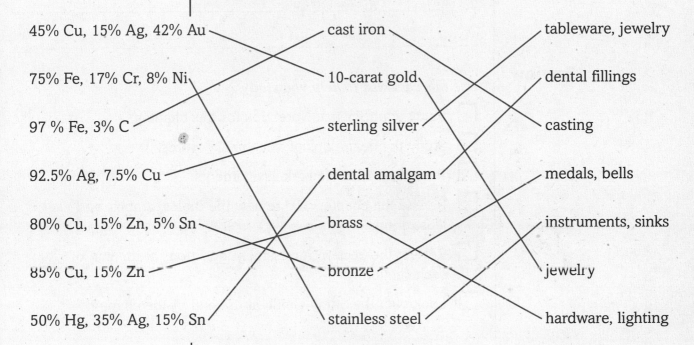

45% Cu, 15% Ag, 42% Au   cast iron   tableware, jewelry

75% Fe, 17% Cr, 8% Ni   10-carat gold   dental fillings

97 % Fe, 3% C   sterling silver   casting

92.5% Ag, 7.5% Cu   dental amalgam   medals, bells

80% Cu, 15% Zn, 5% Sn   brass   instruments, sinks

85% Cu, 15% Zn   bronze   jewelry

50% Hg, 35% Ag, 15% Sn   stainless steel   hardware, lighting

Contrast *a substitutional alloy with an interstitial alloy. Give an example of each.*

In a substitutional alloy, the atoms of the original metallic solid are

replaced by other metal atoms of similar size. The resulting alloy

possesses properties of both of the component metals. Sterling

silver is an example of a substitutional alloy.

In an interstitial alloy, the small holes (interstices) in a metallic

crystal are filled with smaller atoms of another element. The

resulting alloy has properties that differ from those of the original

metal, but are not necessarily more like the properties of the

added element. Carbon steel is an example of an interstitial alloy.

Ionic Compounds and Metals Chapter Wrap-Up

Review

Now that you have read the chapter, review what you have learned. List three important facts about ionic compounds.

1. Accept all reasonable answers._____

2. _____

3. _____

Use this checklist to help you study.

☐ Study your Science Notebook for this chapter.

☐ Study the definitions of vocabulary words.

☐ Review daily homework assignments.

☐ Reread the chapter, and review the tables, graphs, and illustrations.

☐ Review the Section Assessment questions at the end of each section.

☐ Look over the Study Guide at the end of the chapter.

SUMMARIZE   Explain how the atomic properties of an element determine what sort of ion it will form, and what properties a resulting ionic compound will have.

If an element loses one or more valance electron in order to attain a noble gas configuration, it

forms a positively charged ion, or cation. If an element gains electrons to form a stable outer

electron configuration, it will form a negatively charged ion, or anion. The positive and

negative ions are bonded in a regular repeating pattern that balances the attraction

and repulsion of the ions, forming a crystal lattice. The stronger the attraction

between ions in an ionic compound, the harder the compound, and the higher its

melting and boiling points.

Covalent Bonding

Before You Read

Review Vocabulary **Define** *the following terms.*

ionic bond the electrostatic force that holds oppositely charged particles

together in an ionic compound

octet rule states that atoms lose, gain, or share electrons in order to acquire

a full set of eight valence electrons

Chapter 4 **Describe** *the structure of an atom.*

An atom has a dense central nucleus consisting of neutrons and

positively charged protons, which is surrounded by a cloud of

fast-moving, negatively charged electrons.

Chapter 6 **Explain** *the following concepts: periodic trends and periodic properties of elements.*

Periodic trends are the tendencies of the properties of elements to

change in a predictable way as you move across a period or down

a group. The periodic properties of elements are the chemical or

physical characteristics of elements in the periodic table.

Chapter 8 **Identify** *the ions, along with their charges, in the following ionic compounds.*

Li_2S _____ cation: Li^+; anion S^{2-} _____

$KMnO_4$ _____ cation: K^+; anion MnO_4^- _____

Al_2O_3 _____ cation: Al^{3+}; anion O^{2-} _____

Covalent Bonding

Section 8.1 The Covalent Bond

Main Idea ——— **Details** ———————————————

Skim *Section 1 of your text. Write three questions that come to mind from reading the headings and the illustration captions.*

1. Accept all reasonable responses._____

2. _____

3. _____

New Vocabulary   *Use your text to define each term.*

covalent bond — chemical bond that results from sharing valence electrons

molecule — forms when two or more atoms bond covalently

Lewis structure — an electron-dot diagram that is used to show how electrons are arranged in molecules

sigma bond — a single covalent bond between two atoms that share an electron pair in an area centered between the two atoms

pi bond — covalent bond formed when parallel orbitals overlap to share electrons

endothermic reaction — a reaction in which more energy is required to break the bonds in the reactants than is released when new bonds form in the product molecules

exothermic reaction — a reaction in which more energy is released when new bonds form in the product molecules than is required to break the bonds in the reactants

Academic Vocabulary   *Define the following term.*

overlap — to occupy the same area in part

Section 8.1 The Covalent Bond (continued)

Main Idea	Details

Why do atoms bond?

Use with page 240.

Explain *the octet rule by completing the following sentences.*

The __octet__ rule states that __atoms lose, gain, or share electrons to__ __achieve a stable configuration of eight valence electrons, or an__ __octet__. Although exceptions exist, the rule provides a useful framework for understanding __chemical bonds__.

What is a covalent bond?

Use with page 241.

Complete *the following sentences using words or phrases from your text.*

The force between two atoms is the result of __electron-electron__ repulsion, nucleus-nucleus __repulsion__, and nucleus-electron __attraction__. At the point of __maximum attraction__, the __attractive__ forces balance the __repulsive__ forces. The most stable arrangement of atoms exists at the point of __maximum attraction__, when the atoms bond covalently and a __molecule__ forms.

Single Covalent Bonds Lewis Structure of a Molecule

Use with Example Problem 8.1, page 244.

Solve *Read Example Problem 8.1 in your text.*

You Try It
Problem
Draw the Lewis structure for hydrochloric acid, HCl.

1. **Analyze the Problem**
   Write the electron-dot structures of each of the two component atoms.
   Known: H., .C̈l:

   Unknown: __the Lewis structure__ of HCl

   Hydrogen, H, has only one valence electron. Chlorine, Cl, has seven valence electrons. Cl needs one electron to complete its octet.

2. **Solve for the Unknown**
   Draw the electron-dot structure for each of the component atoms. Then show the sharing of the pairs of electrons.

   H.   +   .C̈l: →   H—C̈l:

   __hydrogen__   __chlorine__   __hydrochloric acid__

   __atom__   __atom__   __molecule__

Section 8.1 The Covalent Bond (continued)

Main Idea ———— **Details** —————————————————

3. **Evaluate the Answer**

Each atom in the molecule has achieved a <u>noble gas</u> configuration and thus is <u>stable</u>.

Multiple Covalent Bonds

Use with pages 245–246.

Identify *each bond between the component atoms as sigma bonds (single bonds), one sigma bond and one pi bond (double bonds), or one sigma bond and two pi bonds (triple bonds).*

H−C≡C−H <u>one sigma bond and two pi bonds between the two</u>

<u>carbon atoms; one sigma bond between one hydrogen</u>

<u>atom and one carbon atom</u>

H−C=O
    |
    H

<u>one sigma bond and one pi bond between the carbon</u>

<u>atom and the oxygen atom; one sigma bond between</u>

<u>each hydrogen atom and the carbon atom</u>

The Strength of Covalent Bonds

Use with pages 246–247.

Explain *the factors that control the strength of covalent bonds.*

<u>The strength of a covalent bond depends on how much distance</u>

<u>separates bonded nuclei (the bond length). As the number of shared</u>

<u>electron pairs increases, the bond length decreases. The shorter the</u>

<u>bond length, the stronger the bond.</u>

Define *bond dissociation energy.*

<u>the amount of energy required to break a specific covalent bond</u>

REAL-WORLD CONNECTION Explain how understanding covalent bonding and the chemistry of compounds might help scientists increase food supplies.

<u>Accept all reasonable responses. Possible answer: An understanding of how the genetic</u>

<u>material in foods is bonded together might help scientists encourage foods to pass on genetic</u>

<u>traits to be larger, tastier, or more nutritious in future generations.</u>

The Covalent Bond
Section 8.2 Naming Molecules

Main Idea ——— **Details** ————————————

Scan *Section 2 of your text. Use the checklist below as a guide.*

- Read all section titles.
- Read all boldfaced words.
- Read all tables and graphs.
- Read all formulas.
- Look at all figures and read the captions.
- Think about what you already know about the naming of molecules.

Write *three facts you discovered about the names and formulas of covalent molecules.*

1. Accept all reasonable responses. _____

2. _____

3. _____

New Vocabulary *Use your text to define the following term.*

oxyacid   any acid that contains hydrogen and an oxyanion _____

Section 8.2 Naming Molecules (continued)

Main Idea	Details

Naming Binary Molecular Compounds

Use with Example Problem 8.2, page 249.

Identify *the prefixes for these three binary molecular compounds.*

Ge_3N_2 ___tri___ -germanium ___di___ -nitride

C_2Cl_4 ___di___ -carbon ___tetra___ -chloride

B_6Si ___hexa___ -boron silicide

Solve *Read Example Problem 8.2 in your text.*

You Try It

• Problem — — — — — — — — — — — — — — — — —

Name the compound N_2O_3.

1. **Analyze the Problem**

   Known: ___the compound formula: N_2O_3___

   Unknown: ___the compound name___

   The formula reveals the elements present and the number of atoms for each element. Only two elements are present, and both are nonmetals, so the compound can be named according to the rules for binary molecular compounds.

2. **Solve for the Unknown**

   The first element present in the compound is __N__ , __nitrogen__ . The second element is __O__ , __oxygen__ . The root of this name is __ox-__ , so the second part of the name is __oxide__ . From the formula, two __nitrogen__ atoms and three __oxygen__ atoms make up a molecule of the compound. The prefix for two is __di-__ and prefix for three is __tri-__ . The complete name for the compound is __dinitrogen trioxide__ .

3. **Evaluate the Answer**

   The name __dinitrogen trioxide__ shows that a molecule of the compound contains __two nitrogen__ atoms and __three oxygen__ atoms, which agrees with the chemical formula for the compound, N_2O_3.

Section 8.2 Naming Molecules (continued)

Main Idea	Details

Naming Acids

Use with page 250.

Match *the chemical formulas listed below with the correct acids.*

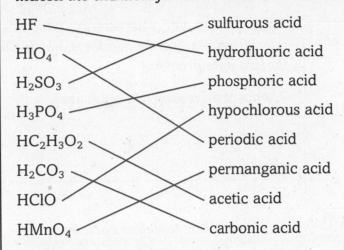

HF — sulfurous acid

HIO_4 — hydrofluoric acid

H_2SO_3 — phosphoric acid

H_3PO_4 — hypochlorous acid

$HC_2H_3O_2$ — periodic acid

H_2CO_3 — permanganic acid

HClO — acetic acid

$HMnO_4$ — carbonic acid

Writing Formulas from Names

Use with pages 251–252.

Write *the chemical formula for the molecular compound names given below. Use the flow chart in Figure 8.12 to help you determine the correct formulas.*

C_2Br_4 dicarbon tetrabromide S_4N_4 tetrasulfur tetranitride

AsF_5 arsenic pentafluoride H_3AsO_4 arsenic acid

$HClO_4$ perchloric acid   HCN   hydrocyanic acid

SYNTHESIZE   Create questions and answers about naming molecules for your own original quiz game. Include topics such as: prefixes and number of atoms; formulas, common names, and molecular names for covalent binary compounds; and formulas, common names, and molecular names for binary acids and oxyacids.

Accept all reasonable responses. _____

_____

_____

_____

_____

Covalent Bonding
Section 8.3 Molecular Structures

Main Idea ———   **Details** ————————————————

Skim *Section 3 of your text. Write three questions that come to mind from reading the headings, illustration captions, and topics for the example problems.*

1. Accept all reasonable responses. _____

2. _____

3. _____

New Vocabulary   *Use your text to define each term.*

structural formula   a molecular model that uses letter symbols and bonds to show

relative positions of atoms

resonance   a condition that occurs when more than one valid Lewis structure

can be written for a molecule or ion

coordinate covalent bond   a covalent bond that forms when one atom donates a pair of

electrons to be shared with an atom or ion that needs two electrons

to become stable

Section 8.3 Molecular Structures (continued)

Main Idea ————

Structural Formulas

Use with pages 253–254.

Details ————————————————————

List *the steps that should be used to determine Lewis structures.*

1. Predict the location of certain atoms.

2. Find the total number of electrons available for bonding.

3. Determine the number of bonding pairs by dividing the number

   of electrons available for bonding by two.

4. Place one bonding pair (single bond) between the central atoms

   and each of the terminal atoms.

Lewis Structure for a Covalent Compound with Multiple Bonds

Use with Example Problem 8.4, page 256.

Solve *Read Example Problem 8.4 in your text.*

You Try It

Problem —·

Draw the Lewis structure for FCHO.

1. Analyze the Problem

Known: the compound formula: __FCHO__

Unknown: **the Lewis structure for FCHO**

Carbon has less attraction for shared electrons, so it is the central atom.

2. Solve for the Unknown

Find the total number of valence electrons and the number of bonding pairs.

[4] valence electrons/C atom + [7] valence electrons/F atom

+ 1 valence electron/H atom + [6] valence electrons/O atom

= [18] valence electrons

[18] available valence electrons/(2 electrons/pair) = [9]

available pairs

Section 8.3 Molecular Structures (continued)

Main Idea ———— **Details** ————————————————————————

Draw single bonds, which represent **an electron pair** each, from the carbon atom to each terminal atom, and place electron pairs around the **oxygen** and **fluorine** atoms to give them stable **octets**.

$$H—C—\overset{..}{\underset{..}{O}}:$$
$$|$$
$$:\overset{}{\underset{..}{F}}:$$

__9__ available pairs – __9__ pairs used = 0

Carbon does not have an octet, so one of the lone pairs on the **oxygen** atom must be used to form a **double** bond.

$$H—C==O$$
$$|$$
$$F$$
_____

3. Evaluate the Answer

Both carbon and **oxygen** now have an octet, which satisfies the octet rule.

Lewis Structure for a Polyatomic Ion

Use with Example Problem 8.5, page 257.

Solve *Read Example Problem 8.5 in your text.*

You Try It

Problem --

Draw the Lewis structure for the permanganate ion (MnO_4^-).

1. Analyze the Problem

Known: the compound formula: _____ MnO_4^- _____

Unknown: **the Lewis structure for MnO_4^-**
_____

Manganese has less attraction for shared electrons, so it is the central atom.

2. Solve for the Unknown

Find the total number of valence electrons and the number of bonding pairs.

1 Mn atom × ($\boxed{7}$ valence electrons/Mn atom) + $\boxed{4}$ O atoms × (6 valence electrons/O atom + $\boxed{1}$ electron(s) from the negative charge = $\boxed{32}$ valence electrons

Section 8.3 Molecular Structures (continued)

Main Idea ———

Details ——————————————————————

32 available valence electrons/(2 electrons/pair) = 16 available pairs + 1 electron

Draw single bonds, which represent an **electron pair each**, from the Mn atom to each O atom, and place electron pairs around the O atoms to give them stable **octets**.

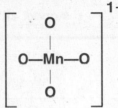

16 available pairs − 16 pairs used = 0

No electron pairs remain available for the Mn atom, so the Lewis structure for the permanganate ion is:

$$\begin{bmatrix} & O & \\ O & -Mn- & O \\ & O & \end{bmatrix}^{1-}$$

3. Evaluate the Answer

All atoms now have an octet, and the group of atoms has a net charge of _−1_.

Resonance Structures

Use with page 258.

Explain *resonance structures by completing the following sentences.*

Each actual molecule or ion that undergoes **resonance** behaves as if it has only **one** structure. Experimentally measured bond lengths show that the bonds are **identical** to each other.

Exceptions to the Octet Rule

Use with pages 258–259.

List *three reasons for exceptions to the octet rule.*

1. A small group of molecules has an odd number of electrons and cannot form an octet around each atom.

2. Some compounds form with fewer than eight electrons present around an atom.

3. Some compounds form around atoms that have more than eight valence electrons.

Covalent Bonding
Section 8.4 Molecular Shapes

Main Idea	Details
	Scan *Section 4 of your text. Use the checklist below as a guide.*
	• Read all section titles.
	• Read all boldfaced words.
	• Read all tables.
	• Look at all pictures and read the captions.
	• Think about what you already know about the shapes and arrangements of atoms in covalent compounds.
	Write *three facts you discovered about the shapes covalent compounds take.*
	1. Accept all reasonable responses.
	2. _____
	3. _____

New Vocabulary *Use your text to define each term.*

VSEPR model — the abbreviation for Valence Shell Electron Pair Repulsion model, in which the arrangement of atoms in a molecule is such that the repulsion of shared and unshared pairs of electrons around the central atom is minimized

hybridization — a process in which atomic orbitals are mixed together to form new, identical orbitals, called hybrid orbitals

Section 8.4 Molecular Shapes (continued)

| (Main Idea) | (Details) |

VSEPR Model

Use with pages 261–263.

Match *the molecular shapes listed below with their corresponding bond angles.*

trigonal planar ———————— 180°

trigonal pyramidal ———————— 120°

bent ———————— 109.5°

linear ———————— 107.3°

octahedral ———————— 104.5°

tetrahedral ———————— 90° (out of plane); 120° (in plane)

trigonal bipyramidal ———————— 90°

Hybridization

Use with pages 262–263.

Label *the hybrid orbitals in the figures below as sp, sp^2, sp^3 sp^3d, or sp^3d_2.*

sp^2

sp^2 sp^2

sp^3d

sp^3d sp^3d

sp^3d

sp^3d

sp^3d_2

sp^3d_2 sp^3d_2

sp^3d_2 sp^3d_2

sp^3d_2

Section 8.4 Molecular Shapes (continued)

Main Idea

Find the Shape of a Molecule

Use with Example Problem 8.7, page 264.

Details

Solve *Read Example Problem 8.7 in your text.*

You Try It

Problem

What is the shape of a SbI_5 molecule? Determine the bond angles, and identify the type of hybrid orbitals that form the molecule's bonds.

1. **Analyze the Problem**

   Known: the compound formula: __SbI_5__

   Unknown: __the shape of the molecule, the bond angles, and__
   __the type of hybrid orbital forming the bonds__

   The molecule contains one central antimony atom bonded to __five__ iodine atoms.

2. **Solve for the Unknown**

   Find the number of valence electrons and the number of electron pairs.

   1 Sb atom × (__5__ valence electrons/Sb atom) + __5__ I atoms × (__7__ valence electrons/I atom) = __40__ valence electrons

   Three electron pairs exist on each iodine atom. This leaves __10__ available valence electrons for bonding. __10__ available valence electrons/(2 electrons/pair) = __5__ available pairs

   Draw the molecule's Lewis structure. From this Lewis structure, determine the molecular shape.

   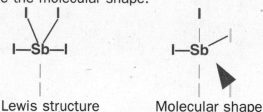

   Lewis structure   Molecular shape

   The molecule's shape is __trigonal bipyramidal__ , with a bond angle of __120°__ in the horizontal plane, and a bond angle of __90°__ between the vertical and horizontal bonds. The bonds are made up of __sp^3d__ hybrid orbitals.

3. **Evaluate the Answer**

   Each iodine atom has an octet. The antimony atom has __ten__ electrons, which is allowed when a *d* orbital is hybridized.

Covalent Bonding
Section 8.5 Electronegativity and Polarity

(Main Idea)	(Details)
	Scan *Section 5 of your text. Use the checklist below as a guide.*
	• Read all section titles.
	• Read all boldfaced words.
	• Read all tables and charts.
	• Look at all pictures and read the captions.
	• Think about what you already know about the strengths and distribution of charge in covalent bonds.
	Write *three facts you discovered about electrognegativity.*
	1. Accept all reasonable responses.
	2. _____
	3. _____
(New Vocabulary)	*Use your text to define the following term.*
polar covalent bond	a covalent bond formed by the unequal sharing of the electron pair
	because there is a difference in electronegativity

Section 8.5 Electronegativity and Polarity (continued)

Main Idea	Details

Electron Affinity, Electronegativity, and Bond Character

Use with pages 265–266.

Sequence *the following elements from the least electronegative to the most electronegative. Use Figure 8.20 for reference.*

__7__ Au

__2__ Y

__1__ Ba

__5__ P

__6__ H

__4__ Te

__9__ O

__8__ I

__3__ Co

Polar Covalent Bonds

Use with pages 267–268.

Draw *the Lewis structure for each of the molecular compounds listed below. Analyze the symmetry of the structure to determine whether or not the compound is polar covalent or nonpolar covalent.*

N_2 : N≡N :   **nonpolar covalent**

CO_2 O=C=O   **nonpolar covalent**

CH_3Cl

polar covalent

Section 8.5 Electronegativity and Polarity (continued)

Main Idea ———— **Details** ————————————

Properties of Covalent Compounds

Use with pages 269–270.

Determine *whether each of the properties listed below is characteristic of ionic compounds, covalent compounds, nonpolar covalent compounds, or polar covalent compounds.*

low melting point _____ covalent compound

very soft solid _____ covalent compound

high boiling point _____ ionic compound

weak interaction between formula units _____ covalent compound

solubility in oil _____ nonpolar covalent compound

very hard solid _____ ionic compound

high melting point _____ ionic compound

solubility in water _____ ionic and polar covalent compounds

easily vaporized _____ covalent compound

strong interaction between formula units _____ ionic compound

Covalent Network Solids

Use with page 270.

Describe *what the network solid for quartz (SiO_2) molecules is like, and how it has a tetrahedral structure similar to diamond structure.*

Silicon has four valence electrons, like carbon. In silicon dioxide (quartz), one of these valence electrons bonds covalently with one of the electrons in each oxygen atom. This leaves two unpaired electrons for the silicon atom and one in the oxygen atoms. If another molecule of silicon dioxide is combined with the first, the two unpaired silicon atoms in one molecule can bond with each of the oxygen atoms in the second molecule. The first molecule now has what is effectively the form of SiO4, which is a tetrahedral molecule. The silicon atom of the second molecule forms two bonds with the oxygen atoms in a third molecule, and so forth. The resulting structure is a crystal with tetrahedral arrangement, similar to the carbon in diamond, and with similar (though not as great) properties of hardness.

Covalent Bonding Chapter Wrap-Up

After reading this chapter, list three key facts about covalent bonding.

1. Accept all reasonable responses._____

2. _____

3. _____

Review

Use this checklist to help you study.

☐ Use this Science Notebook to study this chapter.

☐ Study the vocabulary words and scientific definitions.

☐ Review daily homework assignments.

☐ Reread the chapter and review the tables, graphs, and illustrations.

☐ Review the Section Assessment questions at the end of each section.

☐ Look over the Study Guide at the end of the chapter.

REAL-WORLD CONNECTION

Explain how covalent bonds in carbon account for the vast number of carbon compounds, including those responsible for living organisms.

Accept all reasonable responses. Answers should indicate that carbon, like all elements in its

group, has four unpaired electrons, and thus can form the most number of bonds per atom

before forming a stable octet. These covalent bonds include multiple bonds as well as single

bonds, and because they are covalent, carbon can bond to itself. This provides the basis for

long chains and rings of carbon atoms in molecules, which accounts for the vast number of

organic compounds, many of which are critical to organisms.

Chemical Reactions

Before You Read

Review Vocabulary *Define the following terms.*

ionic compound

compound formed through the creation of an ionic bond between

substances

molecular compound

compound formed through the creation of a covalent bond between

substances

Chapter 7

Explain *how to write formulas for ionic compounds.*

Because no single particle of an ionic compound exists, an ionic

compound is represented by a formula unit, which is the simplest

ratio of the ions involved.

Write *the formula for the following ionic compound.*

aluminum carbonate

$Al_2(CO_3)_2$

Chapter 8

Explain *how to write formulas for molecular compounds.*

Like ionic compounds, molecular compounds are represented by the

simplest ratio of their components.

Write *the formula for the following molecular compound.*

sulfuric acid

H_2SO_4

Chemical Reactions

Section 9.1 Reactions and Equations

(Main Idea) ────────── **(Details)** ──────────────────

Scan *Section 1 of your text. Use the checklist below as a guide.*

- Read all section titles.
- Read all boldfaced words.
- Read all charts and graphs.
- Look at all pictures and read the captions.

Write *three facts about chemical reactions.*

1. Accept all reasonable responses._____

2. _____

3. _____

New Vocabulary *In the left column, write the terms defined below.*

a chemical reaction	*a rearrangement of the atoms in one or more substances to form different substances*
reactants	*the starting substances of a chemical reaction*
products	*the substances formed during a chemical reaction*
a chemical equation	*a statement that uses chemical formulas to show the identities and relative amounts of the substances involved in a chemical reaction*
coefficients	*number written in front of a reactant or product that is used to balance chemical equations*

Academic Vocabulary *Define the following term.*

formula | an expression using chemical symbols to represent
a chemical reaction

Section 9.1 Reactions and Equations (continued)

Main Idea ——— **Details** ———————————————————

Evidence of a Chemical Reaction

Use with page 282.

Identify *three examples of chemical reactions you have seen, heard, or smelled in the last 24 hours. Think about activities at home, at school, or outside. Include any evidence you had that a chemical reaction was occurring.* **Accept all reasonable responses.**

Reaction	Evidence
1. cooking a steak	odor, temperature
2. starting a lawn mower	sound, exhaust
3. turning on a lamp	light

Representing Chemical Reactions

Use with pages 283–285.

Organize *types of equations that can express a chemical reaction. In the second column, list the elements (words, coefficients, etc.) that are used to create each equation. In the third column, rank each equation from 1 to 3, giving a 3 to the equation that provides the most information, and a 1 to the equation that provides the least information.*

Type	Elements	Ranking
Word equations	words	1
Chemical equations	chemical formulas, atoms, and coefficients	3
Skeleton equations	chemical formulas	2

Label *the chemical state each symbol below identifies in a chemical equation.*

(s)   solid state _____

(g)   gaseous state _____

(aq)   water solution _____

(l)   liquid state _____

Section 9.1 Reactions and Equations (continued)

Main Idea ————— **Details** —————————————————————

Balancing Chemical Equations

Use with pages 285–287.

Solve *Read Example Problem 9.1 in your text.*

You Try It

• Problem – •

Balance the chemical equation for the reaction in which fluorine reacts with water to produce hydrofluoric acid and oxygen.

1. Analyze the problem

Known: reactants = F_2, H_2O, products = HF, O_2

Unknown: **Number of atoms needed to balance the equation**

2. Solve for the Unknown

Use the space below to write the skeleton equation:

$F_2 + H_2O \rightarrow HF + O_2$

Count the atoms of each element in the reactants.

__2__ F, __2__ H, __1__ O

Count the atoms of each element in the products.

__1__ F, __1__ H, __2__ O

Insert the coefficient __2__ in front of __H_2O__ to balance the oxygen atoms.

Insert the coefficient __4__ in front of __HF__ to balance the **hydrogen atoms** .

Insert the coefficient __2__ in front of __F__ to balance the **fluorine atoms** .

Write the equation after adding the coefficients.

$2F_2 + 2H_2O \rightarrow 4HF + O_2$

Check that the coefficients are at their lowest possible ratio. The ratio of the coefficients is __1:1:2:1__ .

Write the number of atoms in the balanced equation below:
Reactants: **4 F, 4 H, 2 O**

Products: **4 F, 4 H, 2 O**

3. Evaluate the Answer

The **number of atoms** of each element is **equal** on both sides of the equation. The **coefficients** are written to the **lowest** **possible** ratio.

Name_____   Date _____

Chemical Reactions
Section 9.2 Classifying Chemical Reactions

| Main Idea | Details |

Scan *Section 2 of your text. Use the checklist below as a guide.*

- Read all section titles.
- Read all boldfaced words.
- Read all charts and graphs.
- Look at all pictures and read the captions.
- Think about what you already know about chemical reactions.

Write *three facts you discovered about classifying chemical reactions.*

1. Accept all reasonable responses. _____

2. _____

3. _____

New Vocabulary *Use your text to define of each term.*

synthesis reaction
a chemical reaction in which two or more substances react to

produce a single product

combustion reaction
a chemical reaction in which oxygen combines with a substance

and releases energy in the form of heat and light

decomposition reaction
a chemical reaction in which a single compound breaks down into

two or more elements or new compounds

single-replacement reaction
a chemical reaction in which the atoms of one element replace

the atoms of another element in a compound

double-replacement reaction
a chemical reaction in which ions are exchanged between

two compounds

precipitate
a solid produced during a chemical reaction in a solution

Section 9.2 Classifying Chemical Reactions (continued)

Main Idea	Details

Complete *the following diagrams illustrating each classification of chemical reaction. The first one has been completed for you.*

Synthesis Reactions

Use with page 289.

Synthesis reaction

Substance

Substance ⟩ ——————→ New compound

A + B → __AB__

Combustion Reactions

Use with pages 290–291.

Combustion reactions

Metal, nonmetal, or compound substance

Oxygen ⟩ ——————→ **New compound or oxide**

Decomposition Reactions

Use with page 292.

Decomposition reactions

Compound ——————→ ⟨ Element or **new compound**
Element or **new compound**

AB → **A + B**

Replacement Reactions

Use with pages 293–296.

Single-replacement reactions

Metal or nonmetal

Compound ⟩ ——————→ ⟨ Metal or nonmetal
New Compound

A + BX → **AX + B**

Double-replacement reactions

Compound with cation

Compound with anion ⟩ ——————→ ⟨ **New Compound**
New Compound

AX + BY → **AY + BX**

Section 9.2 Classifying Chemical Reactions (continued)

Main Idea ———— **Details**

Use with pages 289–297.

Organize *types of chemical reactions. The first column in the chart below lists some possible products in a chemical reaction. In the second column, write the type of chemical reaction that is likely to generate each product.*

Products	Possible Chemical Reaction
two different compounds, one of which is often a solid, a gas, or water	**double-replacement reaction**
oxide of the metal or a nonmetal or two or more oxides	**combustible reaction**
two or more elements or compounds	**decomposition reaction**
a new compound and a replaced metal or nonmetal	**single-replacement reaction**
one compound	**synthesis reaction**

ANALOGY Consider the list of metals and halogens and their relative reactivity in Figure 9.13. Using your own experiences, identify people or things that could be ranked according to how they react in a certain situation.

1. (Example) Rank baseball bats by how likely they are to break.

2. Accept all reasonable responses. Rank types of wood by how combustible they are.

3. Rank frozen foods by how fast they melt.

4. Rank teachers by how likely they are to give homework.

Chemical Reactions

Section 9.3 Reactions in Aqueous Solutions

(Main Idea) ——— (Details) ————————————————

Consider the title and first paragraph in Section 3. Based on what you read, what do you expect to learn in this chapter?

Accept all reasonable responses. _____

_____

_____

New Vocabulary *In the left column, write the terms defined below.*

solvent   *the most plentiful substance in a solution*

solutes   *substances dissolved in a solution*

net ionic equations   *equations that include only particles that participate in a reaction*

spectator ion   *ion that does not participate in a reaction*

complete ionic equations   *ionic equation that shows all the particles in a solution as they realistically exist*

aqueous solution   *a solution in which the most plentiful substance is water*

Section 9.3 Reactions in Aqueous Solutions (continued)

Main Idea ——— | **Details** —————————————————————

Aqueous Solutions

Use with pages 299–300.

Connect *English words to their Latin roots. The term* aqueous *comes from the Latin word for water,* aqua. *Use a dictionary to find three words that also come from* aqua, *and list them in the box below together with a brief definition that explains their connection to water.* Accept all reasonable responses. Sample answers:

Word	Definition
aqueduct	used to carry water
aquamarine	a color similar to the color of water
aquatic	having to do with the ocean

Types of Reactions in Aqueous Solutions

Use with pages 300–301.

Compare *a complete ionic equation and a chemical equation.*

A chemical equation is a statement using chemical formulas to describe

the identities and relative amounts of the reactants and products

involved in the chemical reaction. A complete ionic equation is a

chemical equation that shows all of the particles in a solution as they

really exist. Ionic equations differ from chemical equations in that

substances that are ions in solution are written as ions in the equation.

Draw *a circle around the spectator ions in the following equation.*

$2A^+(aq) + 2B^-(aq) + C^+(aq) + 2D^-(aq) \longrightarrow 2A^+(aq) + 2D^-(aq) + 2BC$

Identify *whether each of the equations below is a complete ionic equation or a net ionic equation.*

$A^+(aq) + B^-(aq) + C^+(aq) + D^-(aq) \longrightarrow AD + B^-(aq) + C^+(aq)$

complete

$E^+(aq) + F^-(aq) \longrightarrow EF$

net

$G^+(aq) + HI^-(aq) \longrightarrow GI + H(g)$

net

Section 9.3 Reactions in Aqueous Solutions (continued)

(**Main Idea**)———— (**Details**)————————————

Reactions That Form Water

Use with page 303.

Compare *reactions in aqueous solution that form a precipitate and reactions that form water. Put each of the following characteristics in the corresponding category.*

• can be described with ionic equations

• generates a solid product

• double-replacement reaction

• has no observable evidence

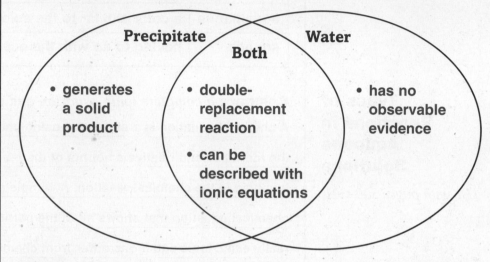

Reactions That Form Gases

Use with page 305.

Identify *three commonly produced gases in reactions in aqueous solutions.*

carbon dioxide
_____

hydrogen cyanide
_____

hydrogen sulfide
_____

State *the evidence that would indicate that carbon dioxide gas is escaping from the solution containing sodium hydrogen carbonate shown in Figure 9.19.*

rapid bubbling
_____

List *the two reactions that occur when any acidic solution is mixed with sodium hydrogen carbonate.*

double replacement
_____

decomposition
_____

Tie-It-All-Together

Sequence *the steps in writing an overall equation.*

1. Write the equation for the first reaction. _____

2. Write the equation for the second reaction. _____

3. Combine the equations with both reactants on one side and both products on the other side. _____

4. Cross out any substances that are on both sides of the equation. _____

What if *ten years from now, you are a chemist working for a government agency that investigates chemical reactions. Read each of the case studies below, and in the space provided, list the type of chemical reaction that you think is involved and any products or effects that you would expect to discover during or after the chemical reaction.*

1. Owners of an industrial plant plan to mix oxygen with existing chemical substances in order to create a new product.

Type of Reaction	Product or Effect
combustion	heat, light, oxides

2. Two vats of chemicals have spilled into a river and created a gelatinous ooze.

Type of Reaction	Product or Effect
double-replacement	precipitate

Chemical Reactions Chapter Wrap-Up

Now that you have read the chapter, review what you have learned. List three facts you have learned about chemical reactions and the equations that describe them.

Accept all reasonable responses.

_____

_____

_____

Review

Use this checklist to help you study.

☐ Study your Science Notebook for this chapter.

☐ Study the definitions of vocabulary words.

☐ Review daily homework assignments.

☐ Reread the chapter, and review the charts, graphs, and illustrations.

☐ Review the Section Assessment questions at the end of each section.

☐ Look over the Study Guide at the end of the chapter.

SYNTHESIZE

Imagine you were asked to give an expert opinion on a magazine article before it is published. The article is on how to make your own household cleansers. You can tell that the author got the ingredients right, and she has amounts in the correct proportion. However, it looks to you like the author mixed up the order in which ingredients should be combined. How would you explain to the author why that matters?

Answers will vary. Adding ingredients in the incorrect order means that unexpected

chemical reactions could occur, which could lead to complications ranging from a finished

product that does not work to the creation of hazardous substances.

The Mole

Before You Read

Define the following terms.

atomic mass | the weighted average mass of the isotopes of an element

atomic mass unit (amu) | one-twelfth the mass of a carbon-12 atom

Chapter 2 | **Write** *the following in scientific notation*

0.00582 5.82×10^{-3}

24, 367 2.4367×10^{4}

400   4×10^{2}

Circle *the significant figures in the numbers below.*

75,600,000

0.00033

3.140

The Mole

Section 10.1 Measuring Matter

Main Idea ——————— **Details** ——————————————————

Scan *Section 1, using the checklist below to preview your text.*

- Read all section titles.
- Read all boldfaced words.
- Read all tables and graphs.
- Look at all pictures and read the captions.
- Think about what you already know about this subject.

Write three questions that come to mind from your reading.

1. Accept all reasonable responses._____

2. _____

3. _____

New Vocabulary *Use your text to define each term.*

mole   the SI base unit used to measure the amount of a substance

Avogadro's number   the number 6.0221367×10^{23}, which is the number of

representative particles in a mole

Counting Particles

Use with page 320.

List *three common counting units and their values.*
Accept all reasonable responses. Possible answers:

1. one dozen eggs = 12 individual eggs

2. one pair of boots = 2 individual boots

3. one ream of paper = 500 sheets

Section 10.1 Measuring Matter (continued)

Main Idea	Details

Use with pages 320–321.

Describe *why chemists needed to invent a new counting unit.*

The number of atoms or particles in a given substance is so great

that it would be impossible to use conventional counting units.

List *three forms of substances that can be measured using moles.*
Accept all reasonable responses. Possible answers:

1. molecules

2. atoms

3. formula units

Converting Between Moles and Particles

Use with pages 322–323.

Analyze *the usefulness of a conversion factor.*

The conversion factor allows us to express a known quantity in

other units. We can switch unit systems because the units in a

conversion factor are equivalent to each other.

Write *the equation for finding the number of representative particles in a number of moles.*

number of representative particles =

$$\text{number of moles} \times \frac{6.02 \times 10^{23} \text{ representative particles}}{1 \text{ mole}}$$

Explain *how you would find the number of moles that are represented by a certain number of representative particles.*

number of moles =

$$\text{number of representative particles} \times \frac{1 \text{ mole}}{6.02 \times 10^{23} \text{ representative particles}}$$

Section 10.1 Measuring Matter (continued)

Main Idea

Converting Particles to Moles

Use with Example Problem 10.1, page 324.

Details

Summarize *Fill in the blanks to help you take notes as you read Example Problem 10.1.*

Problem — · — · — · — · — · — · — · — · — · — · — · — · —

Convert 4.50×10^{24} atoms of Zn to find the number of mol of Zn.

1. **Analyze the Problem**

   Known: number of atoms = **4.50×10^{24} atoms of Zn**

                 1 mole Zn = **6.02×10^{23}** atoms of Zn

   Unknown: mole Zn = **? mol**

2. **Solve for the Unknown**

   the number of atoms × conversion factor = number of moles

   $$\underline{4.50 \times 10^{24}} \text{ atoms Zn} \times \frac{1 \text{ mole Zn}}{6.02 \times 10^{23} \text{ atoms Zn}}$$

   $$= \text{ number of moles}$$

   $$= \textbf{7.48 mol Zn}$$

3. **Evaluate the Answer**

   The answer has **three** significant digits and is less than **10 moles**.

REAL-WORLD CONNECTION

Suppose you were given each of the following tasks. Analyze which task(s) the mole would be an effective unit for counting. Explain your answer.

A. Counting the atoms in a single grain of salt.

B. Counting the grains of salt in a very large mine.

C. Counting the grains of salt in the world.

The mole is an effective counting unit only for vast quantities occupying very small spaces.

Therefore, only Task A can be performed most effectively using the mole as a counting unit. The

grains of salt in a mine or in the world would result in a mole count too small to be of any use.

The Mole

Section 10.2 Mass and the Mole

Main Idea ———

Details —————————————————————————

Scan *Section 2, using the checklist below as a guide.*

- Read all section titles.
- Read all boldfaced words.
- Read all tables and graphs.
- Look at all pictures and read the captions.
- Think about what you already know about this subject.

List four things you expect to learn from the chapter.
Accept all reasonable responses. Possible answers:

1. <u>how to relate the mass of an atom to the mass of a mole in atoms</u>

2. <u>how to calculate the number of moles in a given mass of an</u>

   <u>element and the mass of a given number of moles of an element</u>

3. <u>how to calculate the number of moles of an element when given</u>

   <u>the number of atoms of the element</u>

4. <u>how to calculate the number of atoms of an element when given</u>

   <u>the number of moles of the element</u>

New Vocabulary *Use your text to define this term.*

molar mass <u>the mass in grams of one mole of any pure substance</u>

Section 10.2 Mass and the Mole (continued)

Main Idea	Details

The Mass of a Mole

Use with pages 325–326.

Analyze *molar mass by completing the following statements.*

The mass of one mole of carbon-12 atoms is __12__ grams.

The mass of one mole of hydrogen is __1__ gram and is __1/12th__ the mass of one mole of __carbon__.

The mass of one mole of helium-4 is __1/3rd__ the mass of one mole of __carbon__ and is equal to __4__ grams.

One mole of manganese is equal to __6.02×10^{23}__ atoms of Mn.

Using Molar Mass

Use with pages 327–331.

Organize *the following equations by drawing a line from type of conversion to the correct equation.*

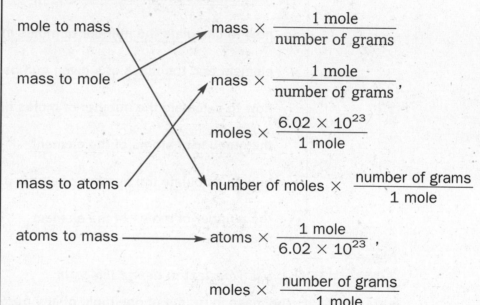

mole to mass

mass to mole

mass to atoms

atoms to mass

$$\text{mass} \times \frac{1 \text{ mole}}{\text{number of grams}}$$

$$\text{mass} \times \frac{1 \text{ mole}}{\text{number of grams}},$$

$$\text{moles} \times \frac{6.02 \times 10^{23}}{1 \text{ mole}}$$

$$\text{number of moles} \times \frac{\text{number of grams}}{1 \text{ mole}}$$

$$\text{atoms} \times \frac{1 \text{ mole}}{6.02 \times 10^{23}},$$

$$\text{moles} \times \frac{\text{number of grams}}{1 \text{ mole}}$$

Section 10.2 Mass and the Mole (continued)

(Main Idea) ——————— **(Details)** ———————————————

Using Molar Mass

Mass to Atoms Conversion

Use with Example Problem 10.4, page 330.

Solve *Read Example Problem 10.4.*

You Try It

Problem – •

Determine how many atoms are in 10 g of pure copper (Cu).

1. **Analyze the Problem**

   Known: mass = **10.0 g Cu**

   Unknown: molar mass

   number of atoms

2. **Solve for the Unknown**

   Use the periodic table to find the atomic mass of copper and convert it to g/mol.

   63.54 g/mol

   Complete the conversion equations.

   mass Cu x conversion factor = moles Cu

   10.0 g Cu × **1 mol Cu /63.54** g Cu = **0.157** moles Cu

   moles Cu × conversion factor = atoms Cu

   0.157 mol Cu × **6.02 × 10²³ atoms Cu/1 mol Cu = 9.45 × 10²²**

   atoms Cu

3. **Evaluate the Answer**

   Restate the answer with correct significant digits.

   There are 9.45 × 10²² atoms of copper in 10.0 g of copper.

The Mole

Section 10.3 Moles of Compounds

Main Idea ——————   **Details** ——————————————————————

Skim Section 3 of your text. Write three questions that come to mind from your reading.

1. Accept all reasonable responses.

2. _____

3. _____

Chemical Formulas and the Mole

Use with pages 333–334.

Describe *the relationship between the mole information of a substance and its chemical formula.*

The mole information of the individual elements shows the ratio

of the elements in a compound. These mole ratios become

the subscripts of the chemical formula.

Mole Relationships from a Chemical Formula

Use with Example Problem 10.6, page 334.

Summarize *Fill in the blanks to help you take notes as you read Problem 10.6.*

Problem -

Determine the number of moles of Al^{3+} ions in 1.25 moles of Al_2O_3.

1. **Analyze the Problem**

   Known: number of moles of alumina = **1.25 mol Al_2O_3**

   Unknown: number of moles = **? Al^{3+} ions**

2. **Solve for the Unknown**

   Write the conversion factor: **2** mol Al^{3+} ions/ **1** mol Al_2O_3

   Multiply the known number of moles by the conversion factor.

   1.25 mol Al_2O_3 × **2** mol Al^{3+} ions/ **1** mol Al_2O_3

   = **2.50** mol Al^{3+} ions

3. **Evaluate the Answer**

   Restate the answer with correct significant digits:

   There are 2.50 mol Al^{3+} ions in 1.25 mol Al_2O_3.

Section 10.3 Moles of Compounds (continued)

Main Idea ———— **Details** —————————————————————

The Molar Mass of Compounds

Use with page 335.

Describe *the molar mass of a compound.*

The molar mass of a compound is the sum of the mass of all

elements in that compound.

Investigate *the process of finding molar mass by completing the table below.*

Number of Moles	Molar Mass	=	Number of Grams
2.000 mol K	39.10 g K/1 mol K	=	78.20 g
1.000 mol Cr	52.00 g Cr/1 mol Cr	=	52.00 g
4.000 mol O	16.00 g O/1 mol O	=	64.00 g
molar mass of K_2CrO_4		=	194.20 g

Converting Moles of a Compound to Mass

Use with page 336.

Analyze *the process of converting moles of a compound to molar mass by completing the table below. Refer to Example Problem 10.7.*

Number of Moles	Molar Mass	=	Number of Grams
2 × 3 mol C	12.01 g C/1 mol C	=	72.06 g
2 × 5 mol H	1.008 g H/1 mol H	=	10.08 g
1 mol S	32.07 g S/1 mol S	=	32.07 g
molar mass of $(C_3H_5)_2S$		=	114.21 g

Section 10.3 Moles of Compounds (continued)

Main Idea	Details

Converting the Mass of a Compound to Moles

Use with page 337.

Investigate *the process of converting the mass of a compound to moles by completing the following.*

Number of Moles	Molar Mass	=	Number of Grams
1 mol Ca	40.08 g Ca/1 mol Ca	=	40.08 g
2 × 1 mol O	16.00 g O/1 mol O	=	32.00 g
2 × 1 mol H	1.008 g H/1 mol H	=	2.016 g
molar mass of Ca(OH)$_2$		=	74.10 g

Conversion factor: __74.10__ g of Ca(OH)$_2$/1 mol Ca(OH)$_2$

g Ca(OH)$_2$ x conversion factor = mol Ca(OH)$_2$

__325 g Ca(OH)$_2$__ × __1 mol Ca(OH)$_2$__ /74.10 g of Ca(OH)$_2$ = __4.39__ mol Ca(OH)$_2$

Converting the Mass of a Compound to Number of Particles

Use with page 338.

Explain *the steps in converting the mass of a compound to number of particles.*

1. Determine the __molar mass__.

2. Multiply by the __inverse__ of the molar mass to convert to __moles__.

3. Multiply by __Avogardro's number__ to calculate the number of __representative particles__.

4. Use the ratios from the __chemical formula__ to calculate the number of __ions__.

5. Calculate the __mass__ per formula unit.

The Mole

Section 10.4 Empirical and Molecular Formulas

Main Idea —————

Details ————————————————————

Skim *Section 4 of your text. Write three questions that come to mind from reading the headings and the illustration captions.*

1. Accept all reasonable responses._____

2. _____

3. _____

New Vocabulary *Use your text to define each term.*

percent composition — the percent by mass of each element in a compound

empirical formula — the formula with the smallest whole-number mole ratio of the elements

molecular formula — specifies the actual number of atoms of each element in one

molecule or formula unit of a substance

Section 10.4 Empirical and Molecular Formulas (continued)

Main Idea	Details

Percent Composition

Use with pages 341–342.

Write *the equation for determining the percent by mass for any element in a compound.*

$$\frac{\text{mass of element}}{\text{mass of compound}} \times 100 = \text{percent by mass}$$

Describe *the general equation for calculating the percent by mass of any element in a compound.*

$$\frac{\text{mass of element in 1 mol compound}}{\text{molar mass of compound}} \times 100 = \text{\% by mass element}$$

Empirical Formula

Use with page 344.

Explain *empirical formula by completing the following statements.*

To determine the empirical **formula** for a compound, you must first determine the smallest **whole number ratio** of the moles of the elements in the compound. This ratio provides the **subscripts** in the empirical formula. If the empirical formula differs from the molecular formula, the molecular formula will be a **simple** multiple of the empirical formula. The data used to determine the chemical formula may be in the form of **percent composition** or it may be the actual masses. When the percent composition is given, you can assume that the total mass of the compound is 100.0 g to simplify calculations. The **ratio** of elements in a compound must be **simplified** to whole numbers to be used as **subscripts** in the chemical formula.

Section 10.4 Empirical and Molecular Formulas (continued)

Main Idea	Details

Molecular Formula

Use with pages 346–349.

Explain *how a molecular formula distinguishes two distinct substances sharing the same empirical formula.*

The molecular formula is more specific because it includes the actual

number of atoms of each element in one molecule of the substance.

Investigate *molecular formulas by completing the steps below. Refer to Example Problem 10.12 in your text.*
empirical formula = $C_2H_3O_2$
molar mass = 118.1 g/mol

Identify the molar mass of the compound.

Moles of Element	Mass of Element/ 1 Mol of Element	=	Mass of Element
2 mol C	12.01 g C/mol C	=	24.02 g C
3 mol H	1.008 g H/mol H	=	3.024 g H
2 mol O	16.00 g O/mol O mol C/mol	=	32.00 g O
empirical molar mass of $C_2H_3O_2$		=	59.04 g

Divide the molar mass of the substance by the molar mass of the compound to determine n.

$$n = \frac{\text{molar mass of substance}}{\text{molar mass of compound}} = \frac{118.1 \text{ g/mol}}{59.04 \text{ g/mol}} = \boxed{2.000}$$

Multiply the subscripts in the empirical formula by n. *Write the molecular formula.*

$C_4H_6O_4$

Section 10.4 Empirical and Molecular Formulas (continued)

Main Idea ——— **Details** ————————————————

Examine *the flow chart below. Write the steps in determining empirical and molecular formulas from percent composition or mass data next to the relevant boxes in the flow chart.*

Express percent by mass in grams.

> Percent composition   Mass of component elements

Find the number of moles of each element.

> $$\frac{\text{Mass of each element}}{\text{Molar mass}}$$

> Ratio of moles of elements

Examine the mole ratio.

> If all are whole numbers

> If not all whole numbers, multiply by the smallest factor that will produce whole numbers

Write the empirical formula.

> Empirical formula

Determine the integer that relates the empirical and molecular formulas.

> $$\frac{\text{Experimental molar mass}}{\text{Mass of empirical formula}} = n$$

Multiply the subscripts by n.

> (Empirical formula) n

Write the molecular formula.

> Molecular formula

The Mole

Section 10.5 Formulas of Hydrates

Main Idea —————

Details ———————————————————

Skim *Section 5 of your text. Write three questions that come to mind from reading the headings and the illustration captions.*

1. Accept all reasonable responses.

2. _____

3. _____

New Vocabulary *Use your text to define the following term.*

hydrate | a compound that has a specific number of water molecules bound

to its atoms

Naming Hydrates

Use with page 351.

Explain *how hydrates are named by completing the table below.*

Prefix	Molecules of Water
mono-	1
di-	2
tri-	3
tetra-	4
penta-	5
hexa-	6
hepta-	7
octa-	8
nona-	9
deca-	10

Section 10.5 Formulas of Hydrates (continued)

Main Idea	Details

Analyzing a Hydrate

Use with page 352.

Describe *an anyhydrate.*

An anhydrate is a compound in which the water that is normally

bound has been driven off.

Determining the Formula of a Hydrate

Use with Example Problem 10.14, page 353.

Solve *Read Example Problem 10.14 in your text.*

You Try It

Problem ──────────────────────────────•

A 5.00 g sample of barium chloride hydrate was heated in a crucible. After the experiment, the mass of the solid weighed 4.26 g. Determine the number of moles of water that must be attached to $BaCl_2$.

1. Analyze the Problem

Known: mass of hydrated compound = **5.00** g $BaCl_2 \cdot x\ H_2O$

mass of anhydrous compound = **4.26** g $BaCl_2$

molar mass of H_2O = **18.02** g/mol

molar mass of $BaCl_2$ = 208.23 g/mol

Unknown: formula for hydrate
name of hydrate

Section 10.5 Formulas of Hydrates (continued)

Main Idea ——— **Details** ——————————————————

2. **Solve for the Unknown**

   Subtract the mass of the anhydrous compound from the hydrated compound.

   5.00 g − 4.26 g = 0.84 g

   Calculate the number of moles of H_2O and anhydrous $BaCl_2$ using the conversion factor that relates moles and mass based on the molar mass.

   $$4.26 \text{ g BaCl}_2 \times \frac{1 \text{ mol BaCl}_2}{208.23 \text{ g BaCl}_2} = \underline{0.0204 \text{ mol BaCl}_2}$$

   $$0.84 \text{ g H}_2\text{O} \times \frac{1 \text{ mol H}_2\text{O}}{18.02 \text{ H}_2\text{O}} = \underline{0.0466 \text{ mol H}_2\text{O}}$$

   Determine the value of x.

   $$x = \frac{\text{moles H}_2\text{O}}{\text{moles BaCl}_2} = \frac{0.0466 \text{ mol H}_2\text{O}}{0.0204 \text{ mol BaCl}_2} = \underline{2}$$

3. **Evaluate the Answer**

   The ratio of H_2O to $BaCl_2$ is __2:1__ so the formula for the hydrate is __$BaCl_2 \cdot 2H_2O$__ , and the name of the hydrate is __barium chloride dihydrate__ .

REAL-WORLD CONNECTION

Explain why hydrates are useful in storage and shipping.

The ability of the anhydrous form of a hydrate to absorb water into its crystal structure allows

it to absorb water from air or liquid, helping to keep solvents dry and protecting sensitive

electronic components from moisture damage.

The Mole Chapter Wrap-Up

Now that you have read the chapter, review what you have learned and list three things you have learned about moles.

Accept all reasonable responses. Possible answers:

1. __A mole is the SI unit used to measure the amount of a substance.__

2. __A mole is the number of representative particles in exactly 12 g__

   __of pure carbon-12.__

3. __Avogadro's number, 6.02×10^{23}, is the volume of particles in one__

   __mole of a gas.__

Review *Use this checklist to help you study.*

☐ Study your Science Notebook for this chapter.

☐ Study the definitions of vocabulary words.

☐ Review daily homework assignments.

☐ Reread the chapter and review the tables, graphs, and illustrations.

☐ Review the Section Assessment questions at the end of each section.

☐ Look over the Study Guide at the end of the chapter.

SUMMARIZE

Summarize the important conversions you have learned in this chapter.

__Accept all reasonable responses. Answers could include the following conversions: moles to__

__particles, particles to moles, moles to mass, mass to moles, mass to atoms, atoms to mass,__

__and mass to moles to particles.__

Stoichiometry

Before You Read

Review Vocabulary *Define the following terms.*

mole   the SI base unit used to measure the amount of atoms, particles, or
formula units in a substance

molar mass   mass in grams of one mole of any pure substance

conversion factor   a ratio of equivalent values used to express the same quantity in different units

dimensional analysis   a method of problem-solving that focuses on the units used to
describe matter

law of conservation of mass   states that mass is neither created nor destroyed during a chemical
reaction, but is conserved

Chapter 9   **Balance** *the following equation.*

$$\boxed{3}\ Mg\ (s)\ +\ \boxed{2}\ AlCl_3\ (aq)\ \rightarrow\ \boxed{2}\ Al\ (s)\ +\ \boxed{3}\ MgCl_2\ (aq)$$

Chapter 10   **Use** *the periodic table in the back of your text to complete the chart.*

Pure Substance	Molar Mass
Carbon	12.011
Sodium	22.990
Oxygen	15.999
Sodium carbonate	105.96

Stoichiometry
Section 11.1 Defining Stoichiometry

Main Idea	Details
	Skim *Section 1 of your text. Write three questions that come to mind from reading the headings and the illustration captions.*
	1. Accept all reasonable responses.
	2. _____
	3. _____
New Vocabulary	*Use your text to define each term.*
stoichiometry	the study of quantitative relationships between amounts of reactants used and products formed by a chemical reaction
mole ratio	a ratio between the numbers of moles of any two substances in a balanced chemical equation
Academic Vocabulary	*Define the following term.*
derive	to obtain from a specified source
Particle and Mole Relationships *Use with page 368.*	**Explain** *the importance of the law of conservation of mass in chemical reactions.* The law of conservation of mass states that matter is neither created nor destroyed in a chemical reaction. Chemical bonds in reactants break and new chemical bonds form to produce products, but the amount of matter present at the end of the reaction is the same as it was at the beginning of the reaction.

Section 11.1 Defining Stoichiometry (continued)

Main Idea———— **Details**———————————————————

Interpreting Chemical Equations

Use with Example Problem 11.1, page 370.

Summarize *Fill in the blanks to help you take notes while you read Example Problem 11.1.*

● **Problem** —·—·—·—·—·—·—·—·—·—·—·—·—·—·—·—·—·—●

Interpret the equation in terms of **representative particles, moles**, and **mass**. Show that the law of conservation of mass is **observed**.

1. **Analyze the Problem**

   Known: $C_3H_8(g) + 5O_2(g) \longrightarrow 3CO_2(g) + 4H_2O(g)$

   Unknown: The equation in terms of molecules = _____

   The equation in terms of moles = _____

   The equation in terms of mass = _____

2. **Solve for the Unknown**

   The coefficients indicate the number of __**molecules**__ .

   The coefficients indicate the number of __**moles**__ .

   Use the space below to calculate the mass of each reactant and each product. Multiply the number of moles by the conversion factor, molar mass.

   moles of reactant $\times \dfrac{\text{grams of reactant}}{\text{1 mole of reactant}}$ = grams of **reactant**

   moles of product $\times \dfrac{\text{grams of reactant}}{\text{1 mole of reactant}}$ = grams of **product**

   Add the masses of the reactants.

   $\boxed{44.09}$ g C_3H_8 + $\boxed{160.0}$ g O_2 = $\boxed{204.1}$ g reactants

   Add the masses of the products.

   $\boxed{132.0}$ g CO_2 + $\boxed{72.08}$ g H_2O = $\boxed{204.1}$ g products

   Determine if the **law of conservation of mass** is observed. Does the mass of the reactants equal the mass of the products? **Yes** .

3. **Evaluate the Answer**

   Each product or reactant has $\boxed{4}$ significant figures. Your answer must have $\boxed{4}$ significant figures.

Section 11.1 Defining Stoichiometry (continued)

Main Idea ——— **Details** ————————————————

Mole ratios

Use with pages 371–372.

Examine *Relationships between coefficients can be used to write conversion factors called* __mole ratios__ .

Example
Given the equation $2KClO_3(s) \longrightarrow 2KCl(s) + 3O_2(g)$

Each substance forms a __mole ratio__ with the other substances in the reaction.

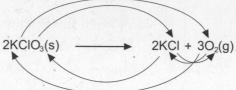

$2KClO_3(s) \longrightarrow 2KCl + 3O_2(g)$

Write *the mole ratios that define the mole relationships in this equation. (Hint: Relate each reactant and each product to each of the other substances.)*

$$\frac{2 \text{ mol } KClO_3}{2 \text{ mol } KCl} \text{ and } \frac{2 \text{ mol } KClO_3}{3 \text{ mol } O_2}$$

$$\frac{2 \text{ mol } KCl}{2 \text{ mol } KClO_3} \text{ and } \frac{3 \text{ mol } O_2}{2 \text{ mol } KClO_3}$$

$$\frac{2 \text{ mol } KCl}{3 \text{ mol } O_2} \text{ and } \frac{3 \text{ mol } O_2}{2 \text{ mol } KCl}$$

You Try It

Draw *arrows with colored pencils that show the relationships of the substances in this equation.*

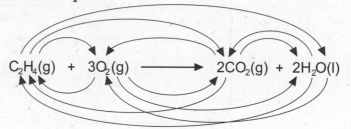

$C_2H_4(g) + 3O_2(g) \longrightarrow 2CO_2(g) + 2H_2O(l)$

Write *the mole ratios for the above equation.*

$$\frac{1 \text{ mol } C_2H_4}{3 \text{ mol } O_2} \text{ and } \frac{1 \text{ mol } C_2H_4}{2 \text{ mol } CO_2} \text{ and } \frac{1 \text{ mol } C_2H_4}{2 \text{ mol } H_2O}$$

$$\frac{3 \text{ mol } O_2}{1 \text{ mol } C_2H_4} \text{ and } \frac{3 \text{ mol } O_2}{2 \text{ mol } CO_2} \text{ and } \frac{3 \text{ mol } O_2}{2 \text{ mol } H_2O}$$

$$\frac{2 \text{ mol } CO_2}{3 \text{ mol } O_2} \text{ and } \frac{2 \text{ mol } CO_2}{1 \text{ mol } C_2H_4} \text{ and } \frac{2 \text{ mol } CO_2}{2 \text{ mol } H_2O}$$

$$\frac{2 \text{ mol } H_2O}{3 \text{ mol } O_2} \text{ and } \frac{2 \text{ mol } H_2O}{2 \text{ mol } CO_2} \text{ and } \frac{2 \text{ mol } H_2O}{1 \text{ mol } C_2H_4}$$

Stoichiometry

Section 11.2 Stoichiometric Calculations

Main Idea	Details

Scan *Section 2, using the checklist below to preview your text.*

- Read all section titles.
- Read all boldfaced words.
- Read all tables and graphs.
- Look at all pictures and read the captions.
- Think about what you already know about this subject.

Write *three facts you discovered about stoichiometric calculations.*

1. **Accept all reasonable responses.**_____

2. _____

3. _____

Using Stoichiometry

Use with page 373.

Identify *the tools needed for stoichiometric calculations.*

All stoichiometric calculations start with __mole ratios__ based on a __balanced chemical equation__. Finally, __mass-to-mole conversions__ are required.

Section 11.2 Stoichiometric Calculations (continued)

Main Idea — **Details**

Mole-to-Mass Stoichiometry

Use with Example Problem 11.3, page 376.

Solve *Read Example Problem 11.3 in your text.*

You Try It

Problem

How many grams of solid iron (III) chloride ($FeCl_3$) are produced when 2.00 moles of solid iron (Fe) are combined with chlorine gas(Cl_2)?

1. **Analyze the Problem**

   Known: **moles of iron = 2.00 mol Fe**

   Unknown: **grams of $FeCl_3$**

   You are given the moles of the reactant, Fe, and must determine the mass of the product, $FeCl_3$, therefore, you will do a mole to mass conversion.

2. **Solve for the Unknown**

   Write the balanced chemical equation. Identify the known and unknown substances.

   $\boxed{2}$ Fe(s) + $\boxed{3}$ Cl_2(g) = $\boxed{2}$ $FeCl_3$(s)

   List the mole ratios for this equation. (Hint: *Draw arrows that show the relationships of the substances in this equation.*)
   Circle the mole ratio that relates moles of Fe to $FeCl_3$.

   $$\boxed{\frac{1 \text{ mol Fe}}{1 \text{ mol } FeCl_3}} \text{ and } \frac{2 \text{ mol Fe}}{3 \text{ mol } Cl_2}$$

   $$\frac{1 \text{ mol } FeCl_3}{1 \text{ mol Fe}} \text{ and } \frac{2 \text{ mol } FeCl_3}{3 \text{ mol } Cl_2}$$

   $$\frac{3 \text{ mol } Cl_2}{2 \text{ mol } FeCl_3} \text{ and } \frac{3 \text{ mol } Cl_2}{2 \text{ mol Fe}}$$

   Multiply the number of moles of Fe by the mole ratio.

   $$\boxed{2.00} \text{ mol Fe} \times \frac{\boxed{1.00} \text{ mol } FeCl_3}{\boxed{1.00} \text{ mol Fe}} = \boxed{2.00} \text{ mol } FeCl_3$$

   Multiply the moles of $FeCl_3$ by the molar mass of $FeCl_3$.

   $$\boxed{2.00} \text{ mol } FeCl_3 \times \frac{\boxed{162} \text{ g } FeCl_3}{1 \text{ mol } FeCl_3} = \boxed{324} \text{ g } FeCl_3$$

3. **Evaluate the Answer**

   The given number of moles has $\boxed{3}$ digits, so the mass of $FeCl_3$ must have $\boxed{3}$ digits.

Section 11.2 Stoichiometric Calculations (continued)

Main Idea ——— **Details** ————————————————————————

Mole-to-Mole Stoichiometry

Use with Example Problem 11.2, page 375.

Solve *Read Example Problem 11.2 in your text.*

You Try It

Problem

How many moles of aluminum oxide (Al_2O_3) are produced when 4.0 moles of aluminum (Al) are combined with oxygen gas (O_2)?

1. Analyze the Problem

Known: moles of aluminum = 4.0 mol Al
_____

Unknown: moles of oxygen = ? mol O_2
_____

Both the known and the unknown are in moles, therefore, you will do a mole-to-mole conversion.

2. Solve for the Unknown

Write the balanced chemical equation. Label the known and unknown.

$$\boxed{4}\ Al(s) + \boxed{3}\ O_2(g) = \boxed{2}\ Al_2O_3(s)$$

List the mole ratios for this equation. (Hint: *Draw arrows that show the relationships of the substances in this equation.*)

Circle the mole ratio that relates mol Al to mol of Al_2O_3.

$$\frac{4\ mol\ Al}{3\ mol\ O_2} \quad and \quad \frac{2\ mol\ Al}{1\ mol\ Al_2O_3}$$

$$\frac{3\ mol\ O_2}{4\ mol\ Al} \quad and \quad \frac{3\ mol\ O_2}{2\ mol\ Al_2O_3}$$

$$\frac{2\ mol\ Al_2O_3}{3\ mol\ O_2} \quad and \quad \boxed{\frac{1\ mol\ Al_2O_3}{2\ mol\ Al}}$$

Multiply the known number of moles Al by the mole ratio to find the moles of unknown Al_2O_3.

$$\boxed{4.0}\ moles\ of\ Al \times \frac{\boxed{1.0}\ moles\ of\ Al_2O_3}{\boxed{2.0}\ moles\ of\ Al} = \boxed{2.0}\ moles\ of\ Al_2O_3$$

3. Evaluate the Answer

The given number of moles has $\boxed{2}$ significant figures. Therefore, the answer must have $\boxed{2}$ significant figures.

Section 11.2 Stoichiometric Calculations (continued)

⟨Main Idea⟩ ——— ⟨Details⟩ ————————————————————————

Mass-to-Mass Stoichiometry

Use with Example Problem 11.4, page 377.

Solve *Read Example Problem 11.4 in your text.*

You Try It

Problem --

Determine the mass of ammonia (NH_3) produced when 3.75 g of nitrogen gas (N_2) react with hydrogen gas (H_2).

1. Analyze the Problem

Known: | **mass of nitrogen gas = 3.75 g**

Unknown: **g NH_3**

You are given the mass of the reactant, N_2, and must determine the mass of the product NH_3. Do a mass-to-mass conversion.

2. Solve for the Unknown

Write the balanced chemical equation for the reaction.

$$\boxed{1}\ N_2(g) + \boxed{3}\ H_2(g) = \boxed{2}\ NH_3(g)$$

Convert grams of $N_2(g)$ to moles of $N_2(g)$ using the inverse of molar mass as the conversion factor.

$$\boxed{3.75}\ g\ N_2(g) \times \frac{1\ mol\ N_2}{\boxed{28.01}\ g\ N_2} = \boxed{0.13}\ mol\ N_2$$

List the mole ratios for this equation.

$$\frac{1\ mol\ N_2}{3\ mol\ H_2} \quad \frac{1\ mol\ N_2}{2\ mol\ NH_3} \quad \frac{3\ mol\ H_2}{1\ mol\ N_2}$$

$$\frac{3\ mol\ H_2}{2\ mol\ NH_3} \quad \frac{2\ mol\ NH_3}{3\ mol\ H_2} \quad \frac{2\ mol\ NH_3}{1\ mol\ N_2}$$

Multiply moles of N_2 by the mole ratio that relates N_2 to NH_3.

$$\boxed{0.13}\ mol\ N_2 \times \frac{\boxed{2}\ mol\ NH_3}{\boxed{1}\ mol\ N_2} = \boxed{0.26}\ mol\ NH_3$$

Multiply moles of NH_3 by the molar mass.

$$\boxed{0.26}\ mol\ NH_3 \times \frac{\boxed{17.03}\ g\ NH_3}{1\ mol\ NH_3} = \boxed{4.42}\ g\ NH_3$$

3. Evaluate the Answer

The given mass has $\boxed{3}$ significant figures, so the mass of NH_3 must have $\boxed{3}$ significant figures.

Section 11.2 Stoichiometric Calculations (continued)

Main Idea —— **Details** ——————————————————————

Stoichiometric Problem Solving

Use with page 374.

Sequence *the steps needed to convert from the balanced equation to the mass of the unknown.*

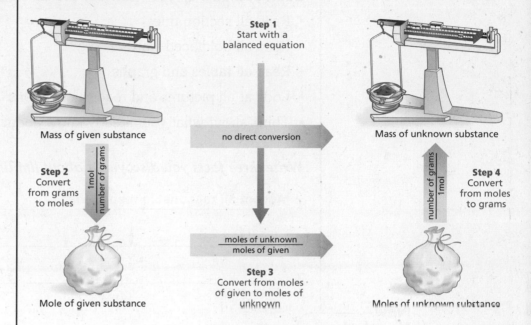

Mass of given substance

Step 1
Start with a
balanced equation

no direct conversion

Mass of unknown substance

Step 2
Convert
from grams
to moles

1mol
number of grams

Step 4
Convert
from moles
to grams

number of grams
1mol

Mole of given substance

moles of unknown
moles of given

Step 3
Convert from moles
of given to moles of
unknown

Moles of unknown substance

Identify *the steps in stoichiometric calculations by completing the summary below.*

1. <u>Write a balanced chemical equation</u>. Interpret the equation in
   terms of <u>moles</u>.

2. <u>Determine the moles of the given substance using a mass-to-
   mole conversion</u>. Use the <u>appropriate mole ratio from the</u>
   <u>balanced chemical equation</u> as the conversion factor.

3. <u>Determine the moles of the unknown substance from the moles</u>
   <u>of the given substance.</u> Use the appropriate mole ratio from the
   <u>balanced chemical equation</u> as the conversion factor.

4. <u>From the moles of the unknown substance, determine the mass</u>
   <u>of the unknown substance using a mole-to-mass conversion.</u>
   Use <u>the molar mass</u> as the conversion factor.

Stoichiometry
Section 11.3 Limiting Reactants

Main Idea ——— **Details** ————————————————————————

Scan *Section 3 of your text. Use the checklist below as a guide.*

• Read all section titles.

• Read all boldfaced words.

• Read all tables and graphs.

• Look at all pictures and read the captions.

• Think about what you already know about limiting reactants.

Write three facts you discovered about limiting reactants.

1. Accept all reasonable responses.
_____

2. _____

3. _____

New Vocabulary *Use your text to define each term.*

limiting reactant   limits the extent of the chemical reaction and, thereby, determines
_____
the amount of product
_____

excess reactant   leftover reactants in a chemical reaction
_____

Section 11.3 Limiting Reactants (continued)

Main Idea	Details

Main Idea

Why do Reactions Stop?

Use with pages 379–380.

Details

What if *you have six slices of bread, three tomato slices, and two cheese slices. How many tomato-cheese sandwiches can you make? Which ingredient(s) limit the number of sandwiches you can make?*

You can make two sandwiches. Cheese is the limiting ingredient.

Calculating the Product When a Reactant is Limiting

Use with pages 380–381.

Organize *information about limiting reactants.*

I. **When do reactants stop?**

   A. Limiting reactant

      1. **limits the extent of the reaction**

      2. **determines the amount of product**

   B. **All remaining reactants are excess reactants**

II. Calculating the product when a reactant is limited

   A. **Find the moles of each reactant**

      1. convert the masses to moles

      2. multiply each mass by the inverse of the molar mass

   B. **Determine the mole ratios for the equation**

   C. **Compare the available moles with the mole ratio to determine the limiting reactant**

   D. Determine the amount of product that can be made with the moles of the limiting reactant.

Determining the Limiting Reactant

Use with Example Problem 11.5, page 382.

Solve *Read Example Problem 11.5 in your text.*

You Try It

Problem

If 100.0 g of sulfur reacts with 50.0 g of chlorine, what mass of disulfur dichloride is produced?

1. Analyze the Problem

Known: **mass of sulfur = 100.0 g, mass of chlorine = 50.0 g**

Unknown: **g disulfur dichloride**

2. Solve for the Unknown

Write the balanced chemical equation.

$$S_8 + 4Cl_2 \longrightarrow 4S_2Cl_2$$

Section 11.3 Limiting Reactants (continued)

Main Idea ———— **Details** ————————————————————

List the mole ratios for this equation.

$$\frac{1 \text{ mol } S_8}{4 \text{ mol } Cl_2} \qquad \frac{1 \text{ mol } S_8}{4 \text{ mol } S_2Cl_2} \qquad \frac{4 \text{ mol } Cl_2}{1 \text{ mol } S_8}$$

$$\frac{4 \text{ mol } Cl_2}{4 \text{ mol } S_2Cl_2} \qquad \frac{4 \text{ mol } S_2Cl_2}{4 \text{ mol } Cl_2} \qquad \frac{4 \text{ mol } S_2Cl_2}{1 \text{ mol } S_8}$$

Multiply each mass by the inverse of molar mass.

$$100 \text{ g } S_8 \times \frac{1 \text{ mol } S_8}{256.5 \text{ g } S_8} = 0.38 \text{ mol } S_8$$

$$50 \text{ g } Cl_2 \times \frac{1 \text{ mol } Cl_2}{70.91 \text{ g } Cl_2} = 0.70 \text{ mol } Cl_2$$

Calculate the actual ratio of available moles.

$$\frac{0.70 \text{ mol } Cl_2}{0.38 \text{ mol } S_8} = \frac{1.84 \text{ mol } Cl_2}{1 \text{ mol } S_8}$$

Determine the limiting reactant.

Because 1.84 moles of Cl_2 are available for every mol of S_8, but 4 moles

of Cl_2 are required for the reaction, Cl_2 will be the limiting reactant.

Multiply the number of moles of the limiting reactant by the mole ratio of the product to the limiting reactant.

$$0.70 \text{ mol } Cl_2 \times \frac{4 \text{ mol } S_2Cl_2}{4 \text{ mol } Cl_2} = 0.70 \text{ mol } S_2Cl_2$$

Multiply moles of the product by the molar mass.

$$0.70 \text{ mol } S_2Cl_2 \times \frac{135.0 \text{ g } S_2Cl_2}{1 \text{ mol } S_2Cl_2} = 94.5 \text{ mol } S_2Cl_2$$

Multiply moles of the excess reactant by the molar mass.

$$0.70 \text{ mol } Cl_2 \times \frac{1 \text{ mol } S_8}{4 \text{ mol } Cl_2} = 0.18 \text{ mol } S_8$$

$$0.18 \text{ mol } S_8 \times \frac{256.5 \text{ g } S_8}{1 \text{ mol } S_8} = 46.1 \text{ g } S_8$$

Subtract the mass of the excess reactant needed from the mass available.

$$100 \text{ g } S_8 - 46.1 \text{ g } S_8 = 53.9 \text{ g } S_8$$

3. **Evaluate the Answer**

The given mass has 3 significant figures, so the mass of the unknown must have 3 significant figures.

Stoichiometry

Section 11.4 Percent Yield

———

Skim *Section 4 of your text. Focus on the headings, subheadings, and boldfaced words. Summarize the main ideas of this section.*

Accept all reasonable responses._____

_____

_____

New Vocabulary *In the left margin, write the terms defined below.*

percent yield

the ratio of actual yield to theoretical yield (from stoichiometric calculations) expressed as a percent

theoretical yield

in a chemical reaction, the maximum amount of product that can be produced from a given amount of reactant

actual yield

the amount of product actually produced when a chemical reaction is carried out in an experiment

How much product?

Use with pages 385–386.

Write *the formula for percent yield.*

$$\frac{\underline{\text{actual yield}} \text{ (from an experiment)}}{\underline{\text{theoretical yield}} \text{ (from stoichiometric calculations)}} \times \underline{100} = \frac{\text{percent}}{\text{yield}}$$

Section 11.4 Percent Yield (continued)

(**Main Idea**)——   (**Details**)————————————————

Percent Yield

Use with page 386.

Solve *Read Example Problem 11.6 in your text.*

You Try It

• Problem –·–•

When 100.0 kg sand (SiO_2) are processed with carbon, CO and 51.4 kg SiC are recovered. What is the percent yield of SiC?

1. **Analyze the Problem**

   Known: **mass of sand = 100 kg   actual yield = 51.4 kg SiC**

   Unknown: **theoretical yield = ? SiC   percent yield = ? SiC**

2. **Solve for the Unknown**

   Write the balanced chemical equation.

   $$SiO_2(s) + 3C(s) \longrightarrow SiC(s) + 2CO(g)$$

   Determine the mole ratio that relates SiO_2 to SiC.

   $$\frac{1 \text{ mol } SiO_2}{1 \text{ mol } SiC}$$

   Convert kg to g.

   100 kg SiO_2 = ___**100,000**___ g, 51.4 kg SiC = ___**51,400**___ g

   Convert mass to moles using the inverse of molar mass.

   $$100,000 \text{ g } SiO_2 \times \frac{1 \text{ mole } SiO_2}{60.09 \text{ g } SiO_2} = 1664 \text{ mol } SiO_2$$

   Use the appropriate mole ratio to convert mol SiO_2 to mol SiC.

   $$1664 \text{ mol } SiO_2 \times \frac{1 \text{ mol } SiO_2}{1 \text{ mol } SiC} = 1664 \text{ mol } SiC$$

   Calculate the theoretical yield. Multiply mol SiC by the molar mass.

   $$1664 \text{ mol } SiC = \frac{40.1 \text{ g } SiC}{1 \text{ mol } SiC} = 66{,}726.4 \text{ g } SiC$$

   Divide the actual yield by the theoretical yield and multiply by 100.

   $$\frac{51.4 \text{ kg } SiC}{66.7 \text{ kg } SiC} \times 100 = 77.0\%$$

3. **Evaluate the Answer**

   The quantities have ⬛3 significant figures, so the percent yield must have ⬛3 significant figures.

Stoichiometry

Stoichiometry and the Stock Market

In the left margin, write the stoichiometry concepts that parallel the daily activities of a Wall Street professional.

theoretical yield

percent yield

excess of reactants

mass-to-mass conversion

limiting reactant

1. A stock analyst keeps a close eye on the earnings of corporations. She has determined how much each company should accomplish.

2. The same analyst tracks whether companies meet expectations or fall short.

3. A grain trader wants to be sure to have 100,000 bushels in reserve for the winter selling season. He places an order for 120,000 bushels because he knows spoilage may damage a percentage of the crop.

4. A livestock futures trader knows that one cattle car holds 10 steers averaging 1200 lbs. each. He wants to bid on an identical car full of sheep, which average about 200 lbs. each. He needs to know how many sheep are on the car.

5. A stockbroker learns that a medical supply company has acquired several tons of a rare silver compound that will allow it to make superior dental equipment. The question is whether the company will have enough of the product to meet the demands of the marketplace.

Stoichiometry Chapter Wrap-Up

Now that you have read the chapter, review what you have learned. Write the key equations and relationships.

Accept all reasonable responses.

_____

_____

_____

Review

Use this checklist to help you study.

- [ ] Use this Science Notebook to study this chapter.
- [ ] Study the vocabulary words and scientific definitions.
- [ ] Review daily homework assignments.
- [ ] Reread the chapter, reviewing the tables, graphs, and illustrations.
- [ ] Review the Section Assessment questions at the end of each section.
- [ ] Look over the Study Guide at the end of the chapter.

REAL-WORLD CONNECTION

Explain how stoichiometry is important to air bags and your safety.

The expansion of an air bag depends on a series of chemical reactions involving heat, sodium azide, and potassium nitrate. If the chemical reactions are not precisely measured through stoichiometric calculations, the air bag may not inflate, or the inflated air bag may be so hard that it can cause harm.

States of Matter

Before You Read

Review Vocabulary *Define the following terms.*

gas | a form of matter that flows to conform to the shape of its container, fills the container's entire volume, and is easily compressed

physical property | a characteristic that can be observed or measured without changing the composition of a sample

Chapter 2 | **Calculate** *the density of a sample with a mass of 22.5 g and a volume of 5.0 cm³. Use the equation: density = mass/volume.*
Density = 22.5 g / 5.0 cm³
Density = 4.5 g/cm³

Chapter 3 | **Describe** *the two essential characteristics that determine the chemical and physical properties of matter.*
The types of atoms present (composition) and their arrangement (structure) determine the chemical properties of a substance. Similarly, the composition and structure of this matter (physical properties) have an impact on how the substance behaves.

Compare and contrast *the chemical and physical properties of gases.*
A chemical property has to do with the Identity of a gas. A physical property has to do with how the gas behaves.

States of Matter
Section 12.1 Gases

Main Idea ———

Details ————————————————

Scan *Section 1, using the checklist below as a guide.*

• Read all section titles.

• Read all boldfaced words.

• Read all tables and graphs.

• Look at all pictures and read the captions.

• Think about what you already know about this subject.

New Vocabulary *Use your text to define each term.*

kinetic-molecular theory	**describes the behavior of gases in terms of particles in motion**
elastic collision	**collision is one in which no kinetic energy is lost**
temperature	**measure of the average kinetic energy of the particles in a sample of matter**
diffusion	**the movement of one material through another from an area of higher concentration to an area of lower concentration**
Graham's law of effusion	**states that the rate of effusion for a gas is inversely proportional to the square root of its molar mass**
pressure	**force per unit area**
barometer	**instrument used to measure atmospheric pressure**
pascal	**SI unit of pressure that is equal to a force of one newton per square meter**
atmosphere	**common measure of air pressure**
Dalton's law of partial pressures	**states that the total pressure of a mixture of gases is equal to the sum of the pressures of all the gases in the mixture**

Section 12.1 Gases (continued)

Main Idea ——— **Details** ————————————————————

The Kinetic-Molecular Theory

Use with pages 402–403.

Distinguish *between the three main physical properties of gas particles by completing the passages below.*

1. Size is very **small** . It is assumed that there are **no** significant **attractive** or **repulsive** forces among gas particles.

2. Motion is **constantly** moving in a **random** pattern. It is assumed that gas particles move in a **straight** path until they **hit an object** .

3. Energy is **conserved** . It is assumed that **mass** and **velocity** impact the **energy** level of a gas **particle** .

Describe *kinetic energy in equation form by completing the table below.*

$KE = 1/2mv^2$	Variable	Definition
KE	kinetic energy	energy of motion
m	mass	amount of matter
v	velocity	the speed and direction of motion

Explaining the Behavior of Gases

Use with pages 403–405.

Describe *the following concepts as they relate to the behaviors of gases by completing the passages below.*

low density—Gases have low density (**mass** per **unit volume**) in comparison to **solids** . The difference in density is partly due to the mass of the **particles** and also because there is a great deal of **space** between gas particles.

compression and expansion—The large amount of **empty space** between gas particles allows them to be **compressed** , or pushed, into a **smaller** volume. Once the pressure is **stopped** , the particles **expand** to the original **volume** .

diffusion and effusion—Because there are no **significant** forces of **attraction** between gas particles, gases **flow easily** past one another. This **random** motion allows gases to mix until they are **evenly distributed** . The movement of **gas particles** past one another is called **diffusion** . The process of allowing a gas to escape from a more concentrated container is called **effusion** .

Section 12.1 Gases (continued)

Main Idea ——— **Details** ——————————————————————

Write *Graham's law of effusion as a proportional statement.*

$$\text{Rate of Effusion} \quad \alpha \quad \frac{1}{\sqrt{\text{molar mass}}}$$

Write *the proportional statement based on Graham's law of effusion that allows you to compare the diffusion rate of two different gases.*

$$\frac{\text{Rate}_A}{\text{Rate}_B} = \sqrt{\frac{\text{molar mass}_B}{\text{molar mass}_A}}$$

Gas Pressure

Use with pages 408–410.

Describe *pressure as it relates to the behaviors of gases.*

Pressure is force per unit area. Gas particles exert pressure when they collide with the walls of a container. More particles in a system exert larger amounts of pressure.

Distinguish *between a barometer and a manometer.*

A barometer measures atmospheric pressure. A manometer measures gas pressure in a closed container.

Explore *the relationship between different units of pressure by filling in the table below.*

Unit Name (unit symbol)	Conversion Ratio: 1 atm = _____	Conversion Ratio: 1 kPa = _____
kilopascal (**kPa**)	101.3 kPa	
millimeters of mercury (**mm Hg**)	760 mm Hg	7.501 mm Hg
torr	760 torr	7.501 torr
pounds per square inch (**psi** or **lb/in²**)	14.7 psi	0.145 psi
atmosphere (**atm**)		0.009869 atm

States of Matter

Section 12.2 Forces of Attraction

Main Idea ———— **Details** ————————————————————

Skim *Section 2 of your text. Write three questions that come to mind from reading the headings and the illustration captions.*

1. Accept all reasonable responses._____

2. _____

3. _____

New Vocabulary   *Use your text to define each term.*

dispersion forces   weak forces resulting from temporary shifts in the density of electrons

in electron clouds

dipole-dipole force   attractions between oppositely charged regions of polar molecules

hydrogen bond   a dipole-dipole attraction that occurs between molecules containing

a hydrogen atom bonded to a small, highly electronegative atom

with at least one lone electron pair

Academic Vocabulary   *Define the following term.*

orient   to arrange in a specific position; to align in the same direction

Section 12.2 Forces of Attraction (continued)

Main Idea	Details

Intermolecular Forces

Use with pages 411–414.

Describe *the difference between an intramolecular and an intermolecular force.*

Intramolecular forces are the forces that hold particles together in

ionic, covalent, and metallic bonds. Intermolecular forces are forces

between or among molecular structures.

Compare and contrast *intramolecular forces by completing the table below.*

Force	Basis of Attraction	Example
Ionic	cations and anions	NaCl
Covalent	positive nuclei and shared electrons	H_2
Metallic	metal cations and mobile electrons	Fe

Compare *intermolecular forces by completing the table below.*

Force	Basis of Attraction	Example
Dispersion	weak forces resulting from temporary shifts in the density of electrons in electron clouds	F_2
Dipole-dipole	attraction between oppositely charged regions of polar molecules	HCl
Hydrogen bond	dipole-dipole attraction between a hydrogen atom and a small, highly electronegative atom with at least one lone pair of electrons	H_2O

States of Matter

Section 12.3 Liquids and Solids

Main Idea ———— **Details** ————————————————————————

Scan *Section 3, using the checklist below as a guide.*

- Read all section titles.
- Read all boldfaced words.
- Read all tables and graphs.
- Look at all pictures and read the captions.
- Think about what you already know about this subject.

New Vocabulary *Use your text to define each term.*

viscosity	measure of the resistance of a liquid to flow
surface tension	measure of inward pull by particles in the interior of a liquid
surfactant	compounds that lower the surface tension of water; also called surface active agents
crystalline solid	solid whose atoms, ions, or molecules are arranged in an orderly, geometric, three-dimensional structure
unit cell	smallest arrangement of connected points that can be repeated in three directions to form a crystal lattice
allotrope	an element that exists in different forms at the same state
amorphous solid	solid in which the particles are not arranged in an regular, repeating pattern

Section 12.3 Liquids and Solids (continued)

Main Idea ————

Details ————————————————————

Liquids

Use with pages 415–419.

Compare and contrast *the following paired concepts as they relate to the properties of liquids by completing the following statements.*

Density and compression: A liquid can take the __shape of its__ __container__ , but its volume is __fixed__ . The density of a liquid is __greater__ than the density of the same substance as a __gas__ . Liquids cannot usually be __compressed__ except under __extremely high__ pressure.

Fluidity and viscosity: Fluidity is the ability to __flow__ . Liquids flow through each other but at a __slower rate__ than __gases__ do. Viscosity is the measure of the __resistance__ of a liquid to __flow__ . The stronger __attractive forces__ slow down the ability to flow, which __increases__ resistance (viscosity).

Viscosity and temperature: Temperature affects the __viscosity__ of a __liquid__ . Viscosity __decreases__ with temperature.

Analyze *the relationship between viscosity, temperature, and change in kinetic energy by completing the table.*

Temperature	Δ KE	Viscosity	Effect in Liquid
increases	increases	decreases	flows faster
decreases	decreases	increases	flows slower
stays the same	no change	no change	no change

Section 12.3 Liquids and Solids (continued)

Main Idea —— **Details** ————————————————————

Explain *surface tension by completing the web diagram below.*

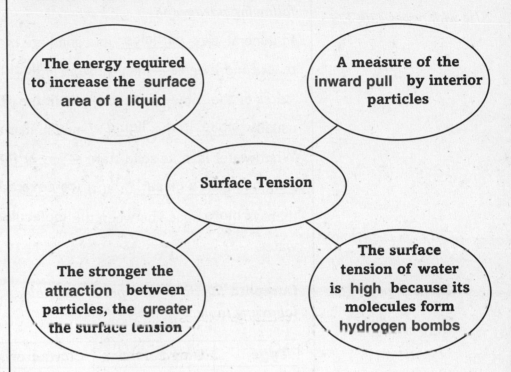

The energy required to increase the surface area of a liquid

A measure of the inward pull by interior particles

Surface Tension

The stronger the attraction between particles, the greater the surface tension

The surface tension of water is high because its molecules form hydrogen bombs

Use with page 419.

Describe *the following concepts as they relate to the properties of liquids by completing the following passages.*

Capillary action is the movement of a liquid up a narrow tube; a function of cohesion and adhesion.

Cohesion is the force of attraction between identical molecules.

Adhesion is the force of attraction between molecules that are different.

Section 12.3 Liquids and Solids (continued)

| Main Idea | Details |

Solids

Use with pages 420–424.

Contrast *the density of solids and liquids by completing the following paragraph.*

In general, the __particles__ in a solid are more __closely packed__— that is, more dense—than those in a __liquid__. When liquid and solid states of the same substance exist at the same time, the __solid__ usually __sinks__ in the __liquid__. One familiar exception is __water__. When water is in its solid state as ice, it __floats to the top__, such as __ice cubes in a glass__ or a(n) __ice-covered lake__. This is because there is __more__ space between the __molecules__ in ice than in liquid water.

Use with page 422.

Compare *the different types of crystalline solids by completing the following table.*

Type	Unit Particles	Characteristics	Examples
Atomic	atoms	soft to very soft; very low melting points; poor conductivity	Group 18 elements
Molecular	molecules	fairly soft; low to moderately high melting points; poor conductivity	I_2, H_2O, NH_3, CO_2, $C_{12}H_{22}O_{11}$
Covalent network	atoms connected by covalent bonds	very hard; very high melting points; often poor conductivity	diamond (C) and quartz (SiO_2)
Ionic	ions	hard; brittle; high melting points; poor conductivity	NaCl, KBr, $CaCO_3$
Metallic	atoms surrounded by mobile valence electrons	soft to hard; low to very high melting points; malleable and ductile; excellent conductivity	all metallic elements

States of Matter

Section 12.4 Phase Changes

Main Idea	Details

Skim *Section 4 of your text. Write a brief summary of the main topics covered.*

Accept all reasonable responses.

_____

_____

_____

New Vocabulary

Use your text to define each term.

vapor pressure

the pressure exerted by a vapor over a liquid

boiling point

the temperature at which the vapor pressure of a liquid equals the

external or atmospheric pressure

condensation

process by which a gas or a vapor becomes a liquid

deposition

process by which a substance changes from a gas or vapor to a

solid without first becoming a liquid

phase diagram

a graph of pressure versus temperature that shows in which phase a

substance exists under different conditions of temperature and pressure

Compare and contrast *the following terms using your text as a guide.*

melting point, freezing point, and triple point

The temperature at which the forces holding the crystal lattice together are broken

so that the solid becomes a liquid is called the melting point. The freezing point is

the temperature at which a liquid is converted to a crystalline solid. The point on

a phase diagram that represents the temperature and pressure at which three

phases of a substance can coexist is the triple point.

vaporization and evaporation

Vaporization is the process by which a liquid changes to a gas or vapor. When

vaporization occurs only at the surface of a liquid, this is called evaporation.

Section 12.4 Phase Changes (continued)

Main Idea	Details

Phase Changes That Require Energy

Use with page 425.

Classify *the types of phase changes by completing the table below. Use Figure 12.23 in your text for reference.*

Phase Transition	Type of Transition
gas to solid	**deposition**
solid to liquid	**melting**
liquid to gas	**vaporization**
liquid to solid	**freezing**
gas to liquid	condensation
solid to gas	**sublimation**

Use with pages 425–428.

Describe *the phase changes that require energy by completing the following outline.*

  I. Melting

    A. Heat energy disrupts __**hydrogen bonds**__.

    B. The amount of energy required depends on __**the strength of the bonds**__.

    C. The melting point is the temperature at which __**a crystalline solid becomes a liquid**__.

    D. The melting point of __**amorphous substances**__ may be unspecified.

  II. Vaporization

    A. In liquid water, some particles have more __**energy**__.

    B. Particles that escape from liquid enter the __**gas phase**__.

    C. When vaporization occurs only at a surface it is called __**evaporation**__.

    D. The pressure exerted by a vapor over liquid is called __**vapor pressure**__.

    E. The temperature at which vapor pressure equals atmospheric pressure is called the __**boiling point**__.

  III. Sublimation

    A. Many solids can become gases without __**entering the liquid phase first**__.

    B. Some solids sublime at __**room temperature**__.

    C. The process of __**freeze drying**__ is an example of sublimation.

Section 12.4 Phase Changes (continued)

Main Idea	Details

Phase Changes That Release Energy

Use with pages 428–429.

Organize *the phase changes that release energy. Identify the phase, describe the process, and identify the reverse process by completing the table below.*

Phase Change	Process Description	Reverse Process
condensation	**process by which a gas or vapor becomes a liquid**	vaporization
freezing	process in which a liquid becomes a solid	**melting**
deposition	**process by which a gas becomes a solid without ever becoming a liquid**	sublimation

Phase Diagrams

Use with pages 429–430.

Explain *how the critical point affects water.*

The critical point is the critical pressure and critical temperature

above which water cannot exist as a liquid. Water vapor at critical

temperature cannot be changed into a liquid if pressure is increased.

Identify *normal freezing point, normal boiling point, critical point, and triple point in the phase diagram for H_2O below. Use Figure 12.30 in your text for reference.*

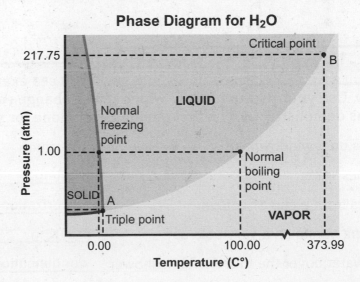

Phase Diagram for H_2O

States of Matter Chapter Wrap-Up

After reading this chapter, list three key equations and relationships.
Accept all reasonable responses. Possible answers:

1. $KE = 1/2mv^2$

2. Viscosity decreases as temperature increases.

3. Melting is the reverse process of freezing.

Review

Use this checklist to help you study.

☐ Study your Science Notebook for this chapter.

☐ Study the definitions of vocabulary words.

☐ Review daily homework assignments.

☐ Reread the chapter and review the tables, graphs, and illustrations.

☐ Review the Section Assessment questions at the end of each section.

☐ Look over the Study Guide at the end of the chapter.

REAL-WORLD CONNECTION

You see examples of phase changes every day. Use your text to identify which phase change each of the following transitions demonstrates. The first one has been done for you.

frost forms on a windowpane	deposition
ice becomes water	**melting**
steam rises from a cup of coffee	**vaporization**
a water pipe bursts on a very cold day	**freezing**
drops of water cover the mirror after a shower	**condensation**
snow melts without leaving a puddle	**sublimation**

Gases

Before You Read

Review Vocabulary — **Define** *the following terms.*

density
mass (m) per unit of volume (V) _____

stoichiometry
the study of quantitative relationships between amounts of reactants

used and products formed by a chemical reaction

kinetic-molecular theory
a description of the properties of gases in terms of energy, size, and

motion of particles

Chapter 9 — **Balance** *the following equation.*

__2__ Fe + __3__ H_2SO_4 ⟶ $Fe_2(SO_4)_3$ + __3__ H_2

Chapter 11 — **Show** *the mole ratios for the following reaction.*

$N_2 + 3H_2$ ⟶ $2NH_3$

a. mole ratio of N to H_2

$$\frac{1 \text{ mol N}}{3 \text{ mol } H_2}$$

b. mole ratio of NH_3 to H_2

$$\frac{2 \text{ mol } NH_3}{3 \text{ mol } H_2}$$

Chapter 12 — **Explain** *how gas particles exert pressure.*

Gas particles exert pressure when they collide with the walls of their

container.

Gases

Section 13.1 The Gas Laws

Main Idea	Details

Scan *Section 1 of your text. Use the checklist below as a guide.*

- Read all section titles.
- Read all boldfaced words.
- Read all tables and graphs.
- Look at all pictures and read the captions.
- Think about what you already know about this subject.

Write *three facts you discovered about the gas laws.*

1. Accept all reasonable responses._____

2. _____

3. _____

New Vocabulary *Use your text to define each term.*

Boyle's law states that the volume of a given amount of gas held at a constant

temperature varies inversely with the pressure

absolute zero a temperature of zero on the Kelvin scale

Charles's law states that the volume of a given mass of gas is directly proportional

to its kelvin temperature at constant pressure

Gay-Lussac's law states that the pressure of a given mass of gas varies directly with

the kelvin temperature when the volume remains constant

combined gas law states the relationship among pressure, volume, and temperature

of a fixed gas amount

Section 13.1 The Gas Laws (continued)

Main Idea _____ **Details** _____

Boyle's Law

Use with page 443.

Solve *Read Example Problem 13.1 in your text.*

You Try It

• Problem

Helium gas in a balloon is compressed from 4.0 L to 2.5 L at constant temperature. The gas's pressure at 4.0 L is 210 kPa. Determine the pressure at 2.5 L.

1. **Analyze the Problem**

   Known: Unknown:

   $V_1 = $ __4.0 L__ $P_2 = $? kPa

   $V_2 = $ __2.5 L__

   $P_1 = $ __210 kPa__

   Use the equation for Boyle's law to solve for P_2.

2. **Solve for the Unknown**

   Write the equation for Boyle's law: $P_1 V_1 = P_2 V_2$

   To solve for P_2, divide both sides by V_2. $P_2 = \dfrac{P_1(V_1)}{(V_2)}$

   Substitute the known values. $P_2 = \dfrac{210 \text{kPa} (4.0 \text{ L})}{(2.5 \text{ L})}$

   Solve for P_2. $P_2 = $ __340 kPa__

3. **Evaluate the Answer**

   When the volume is __decreased__, the pressure is __increased__.

   The answer is in __kPa__, a unit of pressure.

Section 13.1 The Gas Laws (continued)

(Main Idea)——— (Details)————————————————————

Charles's Law

Use with Example Problem 13.2, page 446.

Summarize *Fill in the blanks to help you take notes while you read Example Problem 13.2.*

• **Problem** -·-·-·-·—·—·—·—·—·—·—·—·—·—·—·—·—·—•

A gas sample at 40.0°C occupies a volume of 2.32 L. Assuming the pressure is constant, if the temperature is raised to 75.0°C, what will the volume be?

1. **Analyze the Problem**

   Known: Unknown:

   $T_1 = $ **40.0°C**

   $V_1 = $ **2.32 L** $V_2 = $ **? L**

   $T_2 = $ **75.0°C**

   Use Charles's law and the known values for T_1, V_1, and T_2 to solve for V_2.

2. **Solve for the Unknown**

   Convert the T_1 and T_2 Celsius temperatures to kelvin:

   $T_1 = 273 + 40.0°C = $ **313** K $T_2 = 273 + 75.0°C = $ **348** K

   Write the equation for Charles's law:

   $$\frac{V_1}{T_1} = \frac{V_2}{T_2}$$

   To solve for V_2, multiply both sides by T_2:

   $$V_2 = \frac{V_1\, T_2}{T_1}$$

   Substitute known values:

   $$V_2 = \frac{2.32\ L\ (348\ K)}{(313\ K)}$$

   Solve for V_2.

   $$V_2 = \text{\textbf{2.58 L}}$$

3. **Evaluate the Answer**

   When temperature in kelvin increases by a small amount, the volume **increases** by a small amount. The answer is in **liters**, a unit for volume.

Section 13.1 The Gas Laws (continued)

Main Idea	Details

Gay-Lussac's Law

Use with Example Problem 13.3, page 448.

Solve *Read Example Problem 13.3 in your text.*

You Try It

Problem —

The pressure of a gas stored in a refrigerated container is 4.0 atm at 22.0°C. Determine the gas pressure in the tank if the temperature is lowered to 0.0°C.

1. Analyze the Problem

Known: Unknown:

P_1 = 4.0 atm P_2 = ? **atm**

T_1 = **22.0°C**

T_2 = **0.0°C**

Use Gay-Lussac's law and the known values for T_1, V_1, and T_2 to solve for V_2.

2. Solve for the Unknown

Convert the T_1 and T_2 Celsius figures to kelvin.

T_1 = **273** + 22.0°C = **295** K

T_2 = 273 + **0.0** °C = **273** K

Write the equation for Gay-Lussac's law.

$$\frac{P_1}{T_1} = \frac{P_2}{T_2}$$

To solve for P_2, multiply both sides by T_2.

$$P_2 = \frac{P_1(T_2)}{(T_1)}$$

Substitute known values.

$$P_2 = 4.0 \text{ atm } \frac{(273\,K)}{(295\,K)}$$

Solve for P_2.
P_2 = 3.7 atm

3. Evaluate the Answer

The temperature **decreased** and the pressure **decreased**.

Section 13.1 The Gas Laws (continued)

(Main Idea) ——————   (Details) ——————————————————————

The Combined Gas Law

Use with page 449.

Describe *the combined gas law.*

a single law that includes all of the variables affecting the

behavior of gases—pressure, volume, and temperature

Write *the combined gas law equation.*

$$\frac{P_1 V_1}{T_1} = \frac{P_2 V_2}{T_2}$$

Pressure is inversely proportional to **volume** and directly

proportional to **temperature** . Volume also is **directly proportional**

to temperature.

Use with Example Problem 13.4, page 450.

Solve *Read Example Problem 14.4 in your text.*

You Try It

• **Problem** --•

A gas at 100.0 kPa and 30.0°C has an initial volume of 1.00 L.
Determine the temperature that could support the gas at 200.0 kPa
and a volume of 0.50 L.

1. **Analyze the Problem**

    Known: Unknown:

    $P_1 =$ **100.0 kPa** $T_2 =$? °C

    $P_2 =$ **200.0 kPa**

    $T_1 =$ **30.0°C**

    $V_1 =$ **1.00 L**

    $V_2 =$ **0.50 L**

    Remember that volume increases as temperature increases, and
    volume is inversely proportional to pressure.

2. **Solve for the Unknown**

    Convert the T_1 Celsius temperature to kelvin.

    $T_1 =$ **273** $+ 30.0°C =$ **303** K

Section 13.1 The Gas Laws (continued)

(Main Idea) ———— (Details)————————————————————

Write the combined gas law equation.

$$\frac{P_1 V_1}{T_1} = \frac{P_2 V_2}{T_2}$$

To solve for T_2, multiply both sides of the equation by T_2.

$$\frac{T_2 P_1 V_1}{T_1} = P_2 V_2$$

Multiply both sides of the equation by T_1.

$$T_2 P_1 V_1 = \underline{P_2 V_2 T_1}$$

Divide both sides of the equation by $P_1 V_1$.

$$T_2 = \frac{P_2 V_2 T_1}{P_1 V_1} \quad ,$$

Substitute known values.

$$T_2 = \frac{200.0 \text{ kPa} \times 0.50 \text{ L} \times 303 \text{ K}}{100.0 \text{ kPa} \times 1.00 \text{ L}}$$

Solve for T_2.

$$T_2 = 303 \text{ K} - 273 \text{ K} = 30.0°C$$

3. **Evaluate the Answer**

As pressure **increased** and volume **decreased** in proportional amounts, the temperature remained constant.

Gases

Section 13.2 The Ideal Gas Law

Main Idea ———— **Details** ————————————————————————————

Skim *Section 2 of your text. Write three questions that come to mind from reading the headings and the illustration captions.*

1. Accept all reasonable responses. _____

2. _____

3. _____

New Vocabulary *Use your text to define each term.*

Avogadro's principle states that equal volumes of gases at the same temperature and

pressure contain equal numbers of particles

molar volume the volume that one mole of gas occupies at 0.00°C and 1.00 atm pressure

ideal gas constant (R) an experimentally determined constant; the value of R depends on

the units used for pressure

ideal gas law describes the physical behavior of an ideal gas in terms of the

pressure, volume, temperature, and number of moles of gas present

Section 13.2 The Ideal Gas Law (continued)

Main Idea	Details
Avogadro's Principle *Use with pages 452–453.*	**Explain** *Avogadro's principle by completing the paragraph below.* Avogadro's principle states that <u>equal volumes of gases at the same temperature and pressure contain equal numbers of particles</u>. The <u>molar</u> volume for a gas is the volume that one mole occupies at <u>1.00 atm</u> of pressure and a temperature of <u>0.00°C</u>.

Convert the following volumes of a gas at STP to moles by using 22.4 L/mol as the conversion factor.

$$2.50 \text{ L} \times \frac{1 \text{ mol}}{22.4 \text{ L}} = \underline{\textbf{0.112 mol}}$$

$$7.34 \text{ L} \times \frac{1 \text{ mol}}{22.4 \text{ L}} = \underline{\textbf{0.328 mol}}$$

$$4.7 \text{ L} \times \frac{1 \text{ mol}}{22.4 \text{ L}} = \underline{\textbf{0.21 mol}}$$

Section 13.2 The Ideal Gas Law (continued)

⟨Main Idea⟩ ———   ⟨Details⟩ ———————————————————

The Ideal Gas Law

Use with pages 454–455.

Analyze *the ideal gas law.*

The equation is written $\underline{PV} = \underline{nRT}$

P represents <u>**pressure**</u>

V represents <u>**volume**</u>

n represents the number of <u>**moles**</u> of gas present

R represents the <u>**ideal gas constant**</u>

<u>**T**</u> represents temperature

The ideal gas law states that <u>**the volume of a gas varies directly with the number of moles of the gas and its kelvin temperature and varies inversely with its pressure**</u>. The value of R depends on the units used for <u>**pressure**</u>.

Describe *the properties of an ideal gas.*

An ideal gas is one whose particles take up no space and have no intermolecular attractive forces.

Describe *the properties of a real gas.*

Real gas particles have some volume and are subject to intermolecular forces.

Section 13.2 The Ideal Gas Law (continued)

Main Idea	Details

The Ideal Gas Law

Use with Example Problem 13.6, page 455.

Summarize *Fill in the blanks to help you take notes while you read Example Problem 13.6.*

Problem

Calculate the number of moles of a gas contained in a 3.0-L vessel at 3.00×10^2 K with a pressure of 1.50 atm.

1. Analyze the Problem

Known: Unknown:

$V =$ __3.0 L__ $n = ?$ mol

$T =$ __3.00×10^2 K__

$P =$ __1.50 atm__

$R =$ __0.0821__ $\dfrac{\text{L} \cdot \text{atm}}{\text{mol} \cdot \text{K}}$

Use the known values to find the value of n.

2. Solve for the Unknown

Write the ideal gas law equation.

$$\underline{PV = nRT}$$

To solve for n, divide both sides by RT.

$$n = \frac{PV}{RT}$$

Substitute known values into the equation.

$$n = \frac{(1.50 \text{ atm})(3.0 \text{ L})}{\left(0.0821 \dfrac{\text{L} \cdot \text{atm}}{\text{mol} \cdot \text{K}}\right)(3.00 \times 10^2 \text{ K})}$$

Solve for n.

$$n = \frac{(1.50 \text{ \sout{atm}})(3.0 \text{ \sout{L}})}{\left(0.0821 \dfrac{\text{L} \cdot \text{atm}}{\text{mol} \cdot \text{K}}\right)(3.00 \times 10^2 \text{ \sout{K}})}$$

$$n = \underline{0.18 \text{ mol}}$$

3. Evaluate the Answer

The answer agrees with the prediction that the number of moles will be __less than__ one mole. The unit in the answer is the __mole__.

Gases

Section 13.3 Gas Stoichiometry

Main Idea —— **Details** ————————————————————————

Scan *Section 3 of your text. Use the checklist below as a guide.*

- Read all section titles.
- Read all boldfaced words.
- Read all tables and graphs.
- Look at all pictures and read the captions.
- Think about what you already know about this subject.

Write *three facts you discovered about gas stoichiometry.*

1. Accept all reasonable responses. _____

2. _____

3. _____

Academic Vocabulary *Define the following terms.*

ratio   the relationship in quantity between two things _____

Section 13.3 Gas Stoichiometry (continued)

Main Idea	Details

Stoichiometry and Volume–Volume Problems

Use with page 460.

Indicate *the moles and volume for the reaction below. Use Figure 13.10 as a reference.*

$$2C_4H_{10}(g) + 13O_2(g) \longrightarrow 8CO_2(g) + 10H_2O(g)$$

<u>2</u> moles   <u>13</u> moles   <u>8</u> moles   <u>10</u> moles

<u>2</u> volumes   <u>13</u> volumes   <u>8</u> volumes   <u>10</u> volumes

The coefficients in the balanced equation represent <u>molar</u> amounts and relative <u>volumes</u>.

Volume–Volume Problems

Use with Example Problem 13.7, page 461.

Summarize *Fill in the blanks to help you take notes while you read Example Problem 13.7.*

• Problem —·—·—·—·—·—·—·—·—·—·—·—·—·—·—·—·—·—·—•

Determine the volume of oxygen gas needed for the complete combustion of 4.00 L of propane gas (C_3H_8).

1. Analyze the Problem

Known: Unknown:

V of C_3H_8 = <u>**4.00 L**</u> V of O_2 = ? L

Use the known volume of 4.00 L to find the volume needed for the combustion.

2. Solve for the Unknown

Write the balanced equation for the combustion of C_3H_8.

<u>**$C_3H_8(g) + 5O_2(g) \rightarrow 3CO_2(g) + 4H_2O(g)$**</u>

Write the volume ratio.

<u>**5 volumes of O_2**</u>
<u>**1 volume of C_3H_8**</u>

Multiply the known volume of propane by the volume ratio to find the volume of O_2.

$$4.00 \text{ L } C_3H_8 \times \frac{5 \text{ volumes } O_2}{1 \text{ volume } C_3H_8} = 20.0 \text{ L } O_2$$

3. Evaluate the Answer

The coefficients of the reactants show that the quantity of <u>oxygen</u> consumed is greater than the amount of propane. The unit of the answer is the <u>liter</u>, a unit of volume.

Gases Chapter Wrap-Up

After reading the chapter, review what you have learned.
Match each of the gas laws with its equation.

__4__ Ideal gas law

__3__ Gay-Lussac's law

__1__ Charles's law

__5__ Combined gas law

__2__ Boyle's law

1. $\dfrac{V_1}{T_1} = \dfrac{V_2}{T_2}$

2. $P_1V_1 = P_2V_2$

3. $\dfrac{P_1}{T_1} = \dfrac{P_2}{T_2}$

4. $PV = nRT$

5. $\dfrac{P_1V_1}{T_1} = \dfrac{P_2V_2}{T_2}$

Review | *Use this checklist to help you study.*

☐ Study your Science Notebook for this chapter.

☐ Study the vocabulary words and scientific definitions.

☐ Review daily homework assignments.

☐ Reread the chapter and review the tables, graphs, and illustrations.

☐ Review the Section Assessment questions at the end of each section.

☐ Look over the Study Guide at the end of the chapter.

REAL-WORLD CONNECTION

Explain why the volume of a balloon increases as you blow into it instead of bursting immediately from the added pressure.

As the amount of gas increases, the volume increases. As the volume increases, the pressure

remains the same.

_____

_____

Mixtures and Solutions

Before You Read

Review Vocabulary — *Define the following terms.*

alloy	a mixture of elements with metallic properties that are melted together and allowed to cool to form a solid
solution	a homogeneous, or uniform, mixture containing solids, liquids, or gases

Chapter 3 — **Compare and contrast** *a homogeneous mixture with a heterogeneous mixture.*

In a homogeneous mixture, the components are uniformly mixed and cannot be visually distinguished. In a heterogeneous mixture, the component parts are still visually distinct from each other.

Chapter 8 — **Explain** *why water is a polar molecule. Include a labeled drawing of a water molecule in your answer.*

The polar H—O bonds in a water molecule are not symmetric, which gives water a definite positive end and a definite negative end as shown in the figure below. This makes water a polar molecule.

$$\overset{\delta+}{H} \!\!-\!\! \overset{\delta-}{O}$$
$$\underset{\overset{|}{\underset{H}{}}{}}{}\,{}^{\delta+}$$

Chapter 10 — **Describe** *the relationship between moles and molar mass.*

A mole is the SI unit used to measure the amount of a substance. One mole of a pure substance contains 6.02×10^{23} particles. The mass in grams of one mole of a pure substance is its molar mass.

Mixtures and Solutions

Section 14.1 Types of Mixtures

Main Idea ————

Details ————————————————————————

Scan *Section 1 of your text, using the checklist below as a guide.*

- Read all section titles.
- Read all boldfaced words.
- Read all tables and graphs.
- Look at all pictures and read the captions.
- Think about what you already know about solutions.

Identify *the unifying theme of this section.*

Mixtures can be classified according to many properties.

New Vocabulary *Use your text to define each term.*

suspension   a mixture containing particles that settle out if left undisturbed

colloid   a mixture containing particles whose diameters range between 1nm

and 1000nm

Brownian motion   random movement of colloid particles resulting from the collision of

the particles of the dispersion medium with the dispersed particles

Tyndall effect   the scattering of light by colloidal particles

Compare and contrast *soluble and insoluble substances.*

Soluble means a substance that can dissolve in a solvent. Insoluble

substances do not dissolve in a solvent.

Compare and contrast *miscible and immiscible liquids.*

Miscible liquids are soluble in each other whereas immiscible liquids

do not dissolve in each other.

Section 14.1 Types of Mixtures (continued)

Main Idea	Details

Suspensions

Use with page 476.

List *three properties of a suspension.*

1. Particles separate from the solvent upon standing.

2. Particles can be separated out by filtering.

3. Some separate into distinct layers.

State *three examples of suspensions.*

1. Accept all reasonable responses. Possible answers: muddy water

2. paint

3. orange juice with pulp

Colloids

Use with pages 477–479.

Identify *four properties of a colloid.*

1. The most abundant substance is the dispersion medium.

2. Particles do not settle nor can they be filtered out.

3. Particles display Brownian motion.

4. Particles display the Tyndall effect.

Section 14.1 Types of Mixtures (continued)

Main Idea ——— **Details** ————————————————

Explain *why particles in Brownian motion do not settle out.*

Dispersed particles in Brownian motion do not settle out because

they have polar or charged atomic groups on their surfaces that

attract the positively or negatively charged areas of the dispersing-

medium particles. This results in the formation of electrostatic layers

around the particles that repel each other when the dispersed

particles collide. Therefore, the particles remain in suspension.

Identify *each of the following mixtures as a suspension, dilute colloid, or concentrated colloid. Base your answers on the property described.*

Property	Type of Solution
cloudy mixture with particles that move erratically	concentrated colloid
large particles with thixotropic behavior	suspension
clear mixture with particles that scatter light	dilute colloid

REAL-WORLD CONNECTION Describe the properties of fog in terms of being a mixture and why those properties make driving through fog so dangerous.

Fog is a heterogeneous mixture of small liquid particles dispersed in a gas. The particles are

in the size range of a colloid. As a colloid, fog displays the Tyndall effect. The light beam from

a car is scattered. With no direct light, it is hard to see in the distance.

Mixtures and Solutions
Section 14.2 Solution Concentration

(Main Idea) ─────── **(Details)** ──────────────────────

Scan *Section 2 of your text, using the checklist below as a guide.*

- Read all section titles.
- Read all boldfaced words.
- Read all tables and graphs.
- Look at all pictures and read the captions.
- Think about what you already know about this subject.

Write *three facts you discovered about solutions.*

1. Accept all reasonable responses. Possible answers: the state of

   concentrations of solutions can be described In five quantitative ways

2. concentrations of solutions are expressed as fractions or percentages

3. molarity is a common unIt of solution concentration

(New Vocabulary) *Use your text to define these terms.*

concentration   a measure of how much solute is dissolved in a specific amount of

solvent or solution

molarity   the number of moles of solute dissolved per liter of solution

molality   the ratio of the number of moles of solute dissolved in one kilogram

of solvent

mole fraction   the ratio of the number of moles of solute in solution to the total

number of moles of solute and solvent

(Academic Vocabulary) *Define the following term.*

concentrated   less dilute or diffuse

Section 14.2 Solution Concentration (continued)

Main Idea	Details

Expressing Concentration

Use with pages 480–481.

Analyze *the similarities in all of the concentration ratios shown in Table 14.3 in your text.*

Regardless of the description, all of the ratios involve dividing the quantity of the solute by the quantity of the solution, and multiplying by 100.

Write *the equation for determining percent by mass.*

$$\text{Percent by mass} = \frac{\text{mass of solute}}{\text{mass of solution}} \times 100$$

Calculate Percent by Mass

Use with Example Problem 14.1, page 481.

Summarize *Fill in the blanks to help you take notes as you read Example Problem 14.1.*

Problem --·--·--·--·--·--·--·--·--·--·--·--·--·--·--·--·--•

Determine the percent by mass of 3.6 g NaCl in 100.0 g H_2O.

1. **Analyze the Problem**
   List the knowns and unknowns.

   Known: Unknown:

   mass of solute = **3.6 g NaCl**   percent by mass = ?

   mass of solvent = **100.0 g H_2O**

2. **Solve for the Unknown**
   Find the mass of the solution.

   mass of solution = grams of solute + grams of solvent

   mass of solution = 3.6 g + **100.0 g** = **103.6 g**

   Substitute the known values into the percent by mass equation.

   percent by mass = $\dfrac{\text{3.6 g}}{\text{103.6 g}} \times 100 = 3.5\%$

3. **Evaluate the Answer**

   The answer should be a small percent, to match the small quantity of **solute**. The mass of sodium chloride was given in two significant figures, therefore, the answer should have **two** significant figures.

Section 14.2 Solution Concentration (continued)

Main Idea	Details

Molarity

Use with pages 482–485.

Describe *how to calculate the molarity of a solution by completing the following statements.*

To calculate the <u>**molarity**</u> of a solution, you must know the amount of dissolved <u>**solute**</u> and the volume of <u>**solution**</u>. The following equation is used: molarity (M) = <u>**moles**</u> of solute/liters of <u>**solution**</u>.

Explain *why you may need less than one liter of water to prepare a molar solution of one liter.*

<u>**The amount of solute adds volume to the solution.**</u>

Write *the expression that describes the relationship between a stock solution and a dilute solution.*

<u>$M_1V_1 = M_2V_2$</u>

M_1 = <u>**the molarity of the stock solution**</u>

V_1 = <u>**the volume of the stock solution**</u>

M_2 = <u>**the molarity of the dilute solution**</u>

V_2 = <u>**the volume of the dilute solution**</u>

Section 14.2 Solution Concentration (continued)

Main Idea	Details

Molality and Mole Fraction

Use with pages 487–488.

Explain *how the volume and mass of a solution change with temperature.*

The volume may **expand** when heated or **contract** when cooled.

The mass of the solution **does not** change.

Write *the mole fraction equations for a solvent (X_A) and a solute (X_B) below.*

$$X_A = \frac{n_A}{n_A + n_B} \qquad X_B = \frac{n_B}{n_A + n_B}$$

Evaluate *the mole fraction for the values given in problem 14.4 on page 487 of your text. The number of moles for 100 g H_2O is given.*

$$n_A = 5.55 \text{ mol } H_2O \qquad n_B = \underline{0.077} \text{ mol NaCl}$$

$$X_{H_2O} = \frac{5.55 \text{ mol } H_2O}{(5.55 \text{ mol } H_2O + 0.077 \text{ mol NaCl})} = \underline{0.987}$$

$$X_{NaCL} = \frac{0.077 \text{ mol NaCl}}{(5.55 \text{ mol } H_2O + 0.077 \text{ mol NaCl})} = \underline{0.013}$$

$$X_{H_2O} + X_{NaCl} = 1.000$$

$$\underline{0.987} + \underline{0.013} = 1.000$$

REAL-WORLD CONNECTION

Describe how the mole fractions for a solution are similar to the pieces of a pie.

Each mole fraction is a percent of the whole solution, just as each piece of pie is a percent of

the whole pie.

_____

Mixtures and Solutions

Section 14.3 Factors Affecting Solvation

Main Idea ———— **Details** ———————————————————————————

Skim *Section 3 of your text. List three main ideas of the section.*

1. Accept all reasonable responses.

2. _____

3. _____

New Vocabulary *Use your text to define each term.*

solvation — the process of surrounding solute particles with solvent particles to form a solution

heat of solution — the overall energy change that occurs during the solution formation process

supersaturated solution — a solution that contains more dissolved solute than a saturated solution

at the same temperature

Henry's law — states that at a given temperature, the solubility (S) of a gas in a liquid

Is directly proportional to the pressure (P) of the gas above the liquid

Compare and contrast *saturated solutions and unsaturated solutions.*

Saturated solutions contain the maximum amount of dissolved solute at

a specific temperature and pressure, while unsaturated solutions

contain less dissolved solute for a given temperature and pressure.

Section 14.3 Factors Affecting Solvation (continued)

| Main Idea | Details |

The Solvation Process

Use with pages 489–492.

Describe *solutions by completing the following statements.*

A solution may exist in gas, solid, or liquid form, depending on the state of its **solvent**. Some combinations of substances easily form **solutions** and others do not. A substance that does not **dissolve** in a solvent is **insoluble** in that solvent.

Write *the general rule to determine if solvation will occur.*

Like dissolves like.

List *three factors that must be known about component substances to determine if solvation will occur.*

1. the polarity of particles

2. bonding type

3. intermolecular forces between particles

Sequence *the steps required for a sodium chloride crystal to dissolve in water.*

__3__ The charged ends of water molecules attract the positive Na ions and the negative Cl ions.

__5__ The ions from the crystal break away from the surface.

__2__ Water molecules collide with the surface of the crystal.

__1__ NaCl crystals are placed in water.

__6__ Solvation continues until the entire crystal has dissolved.

__4__ The attraction between the dipoles and the ions are stronger than the attractions among the ions in the crystal.

Section 14.3 Factors Affecting Solvation (continued)

Main Idea	Details
Factors That Affect Solvation *Use with page 492.*	**Organize** *the following table on factors that can increase the rate of solvation by increasing the number of collisions.*

Factor	Increase Collisions By
agitating the mixture	moving dissolved solute particles away from the contact surfaces more quickly
breaking particles into smaller pieces	increasing the surface area where collisions can occur
increasing temperature of the solvent	increasing the kinetic energy of the particles

Solubility

Use with pages 493–496.

Explain *how solubility is expressed in units of measurement.*

grams of solute/100 g of solute
_____

Review *Table 14.4 in your text to determine the solubility of the following compounds in water.*

Ca(OH)$_2$ at 20°C   0.173 g/100 g H$_2$O
_____

KCl at 60°C   45.8 g/100 g H$_2$O
_____

Describe *each of these solubility states.*

State	Description
continuing solvation	the solvation rate is greater than the crystallization rate
dynamic equilibrium	the solvation rate is equal to the crystallization rate
saturated solution	the overall amount of dissolved solute remains constant
unsaturated solution	more solute can be dissolved in the solution

Section 14.3 Factors Affecting Solvation (continued)

Main Idea ——— **Details** ————————————————————

Describe *how solubility changes with temperature for most substances.*

Solubility increases as temperature increases.

Explain *why some gases are less soluble as temperature increases.*

Gas particles escape from the solution more readily as temperature

increases.

Describe *the relationship between solubility and pressure.*

Solubility increases as external pressure increases.

Write *the equation for Henry's law.*

$$\frac{S_1}{P_1} = \frac{S_2}{P_2}$$

Henry's Law

Use with Example Problem 14.5, page 497.

Summarize *Fill in the blanks to help you take notes while you read Example Problem 14.5.*

• Problem –––––––––––––––––––––––––––––––––––––––•

Find how much of a gas will dissolve in 1.0 L of water at 1.0 atm, if 0.85 g of that gas will dissolve in 1.0 L of water at 4.0 atm and temperature does not change.

1. **Analyze the Problem**
   List the knowns and unknowns.
   Known: Unknown:

   $S_1 =$ **0.85 g/L**

   $P_1 =$ **4.0 atm** $S_2 =$ **? g/L**

   $P_2 =$ **1.0 atm**

2. **Solve for the Unknown**
   Rearrange Henry's Law to solve for S_2.

   $S_2 =$ **$S_1(P_2/P_1)$**

   Substitute known values and solve.

   $S_2 =$ **0.85 g/L** $\frac{(1.0 \text{ atm})}{(4.0 \text{ atm})} =$ **0.21 g/L**

3. **Evaluate the Answer**

   The solubility **decreased** as expected due to the **decrease** in

   pressure.

Mixtures and Solutions

Section 14.4 Colligative Properties of Solutions

Main Idea	Details
	Scan *Section 4 of your text, using the checklist below as a guide.*
	• Read all section titles.
	• Read all boldfaced words.
	• Read all tables and graphs.
	• Look at all pictures and read the captions.
	• Think about what you already know about solutions.
	Write two questions that you would want answers to based on your reading.
	1. Accept all reasonable responses.
	2. _____
New Vocabulary	*Use your text to define each term.*
colligative property	physical property of solutions that are affected by the number of particles but not the identity of the dissolved solute particles; colligative means "depending on the collection"
vapor pressure lowering	the decrease in vapor pressure caused by the addition of solute particles into a solvent
boiling point elevation	the temperature difference between a solution's boiling point and a pure solvent's boiling point
freezing point depression	the temperature difference between a solution's freezing point and the freezing point of its pure solvent
osmosis	the diffusion of solvent particles across a semipermeable membrane from an area of higher solvent concentration to an area of lower solvent concentration
osmotic pressure	the amount of additional pressure caused by water molecules that move back across a membrane into a solution

Section 14.4 Colligative Properties of Solutions (continued)

Main Idea	Details

Electrolytes and Colligative Properties

Use with pages 498–499.

Compare and contrast *electrolytes and nonelectrolytes.*

Substances like sodium chloride that <u>ionize</u> in water and conduct an <u>electric current</u> are called <u>electrolytes</u>. Substances like sucrose that dissolve in water but do not <u>ionize</u> and do not conduct an electric current are called <u>nonelectrolytes</u>.

Vapor Pressure Lowering

Use with page 499.

Summarize *why vapor pressure lowering is a colligative property. Include an explanation of vapor pressure.*

<u>Vapor pressure is the pressure exerted in a closed container by liquid</u>

<u>particles that escape the surface of the liquid and become a gas. When</u>

<u>a nonvolatile solute is dissolved in a solution, the surface area is</u>

<u>occupied by a mix of solute and solvent particles, leaving less surface</u>

<u>area for the solvent particles to escape the surface. This lowers the</u>

<u>vapor pressure. Since vapor pressure lowering is due to the number of</u>

<u>solute particles in solution, it is a colligative property.</u>

Boiling Point Elevation

Use with page 500.

Explain *boiling point elevation by completing the following statements.*

A liquid boils when its <u>vapor pressure</u> equals <u>atmospheric pressure</u>. Adding a nonvolatile solute lowers the solvent's <u>vapor</u> pressure. More <u>kinetic</u> energy must be added to reach the solvent's <u>boiling point</u>. The greater the number of <u>solute</u> particles in the solution, the greater the <u>boiling point</u> elevation.

Section 14.4 Colligative Properties of Solutions (continued)

Main Idea ———

Freezing Point Depression

Use with pages 501–502.

Details————————————————

Describe *why the freezing point changes when a solute is added to a solution.*

At a solvent's freezing point, the particles no longer have the kinetic

energy to overcome the interparticle attractive forces and form a

more organized structure. Adding solute particles interferes with the

attractive forces among the solvent particles and prevents the

solvent from freezing at its normal freezing point.

Osmotic Pressure

Use with page 504.

Evaluate *the diagram of a semipermeable membrane separating a sucrose-water solution on one side and water on the other side. Draw an arrow to show in which direction more water will flow and circle the side which has the greater osmotic pressure.*

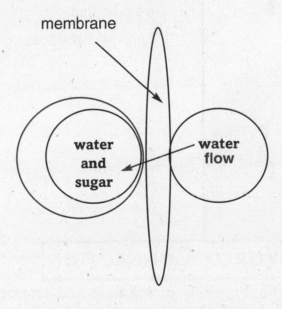

Mixtures and Solutions Chapter Wrap-Up

Now that you have read the chapter, review what you have learned and write the key equations and relationships.

Accept all reasonable responses.

_____

_____

Review *Use this checklist to help you study.*

- ☐ Study your Science Notebook for this chapter.
- ☐ Study the definitions of vocabulary words.
- ☐ Review daily homework assignments.
- ☐ Reread the chapter and review the tables, graphs, and illustrations.
- ☐ Review the Section Assessment questions at the end of each section.
- ☐ Look over the Study Guide at the end of the chapter.

REAL-WORLD CONNECTION

Identify four ways in which an understanding of the properties of solutions and heterogenous mixtures can be applied to your own life. **Accept all reasonable responses. Possible answers:**

1. mixing paint
2. diluting a cleaning solution
3. making a cup of hot chocolate
4. caring for an aquarium

Energy and Chemical Change

Before You Read

Review Vocabulary *Define the following terms.*

chemical equation	a statement using chemical formulas to describe the identities and relative amounts of the reactants and products involved in a chemical reaction
mole	the SI base unit used to measure the amount of a substance, abbreviated mol; one mole is the amount of a pure substance that contains 6.02×10^{23} representative particles

Chapter 10 **Describe** *the equation you would use to convert mass in grams to moles.*

$$\text{mass} \times \frac{1 \text{ mole}}{\text{number of grams}} = \text{number of moles}$$

Chapter 12 **Identify** *the three characteristics of particles about which the kinetic-molecular theory makes assumptions.*

1. particle size

2. particle motion

3. particle energy

Write the equation that represents the kinetic energy of a particle.

$KE = 1/2mv^2$

Energy and Chemical Change

Section 15.1 Energy

《Main Idea》 ———— **《Details》**———————————————————

Skim *Section 1 of your text. Write two facts you discovered about energy.* **Accept all reasonable responses. Sample answers:**

1. Potential and kinetic energy can be applied to physical and

   chemical systems.

2. In any chemical or physical process, energy can be converted

   from one form to another but cannot be created or destroyed.

New Vocabulary *Use your text to define each term.*

energy   the ability to do work or produce heat

law of conservation of energy   law stating that in any chemical reaction or physical process, energy can be

converted from one form to another, but it is neither created nor destroyed

chemical potential energy   the energy stored in a substance because of its composition

heat   energy that is in the process of flowing from a warmer object to a

cooler object

calorie   the amount of heat required to raise the temperature of one gram of

pure water one degree Celsius (1°C)

joule   SI unit for heat and energy; one joule is equivalent to 0.2390 calories

specific heat   the amount of heat required to raise the temperature of one gram of

a substance by one degree Celsius

Section 15.1 Energy (continued)

Main Idea	**Details**

The Nature of Energy

Use with pages 516–518.

Compare and contrast *kinetic energy with potential energy.*

Kinetic energy is the energy of motion. Potential energy is energy of

the composition or position of an object.

On the curve below that represents the skier on a ski slope on page 516, label the place of greatest kinetic energy A, least kinetic energy B, greatest potential energy C, and least potential energy D.

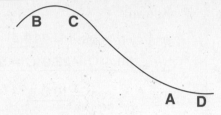

Describe *the skier above as a function of the law of conservation of energy.*

Before the skier starts, there is potential energy that is converted to

kinetic energy, then to potential energy as the skier stops.

Energy changes form.

Explain *chemical potential energy.*

Chemical **potential** energy of a substance is a result of the arrange-

ment of its **atoms** and the strength of the **chemical bonds** joining

the atoms. During some **chemical** reactions, such as burning **fuel**,

much of the potential energy may be released as **heat**. Some of the

energy may be converted to work, which is a form of **kinetic** energy.

Specific Heat

Use with pages 519–520.

Identify *each symbol in the equation for specific heat.*

$q = c \times m \times \Delta T$

q represents heat absorbed or released

c represents the specific heat of the substance

m represents mass of a sample in grams

ΔT represents a change in temperature

Section 15.1 Energy (continued)

Main Idea	Details

Calculate Specific Heat

Use with Example Problem 15.2, page 521.

Summarize. *Fill in the blanks to help you take notes while you read Example Problem 15.2.*

• Problem

The temperature of a sample of iron with a mass of 10.0 g changed from 50.4°C to 25.0°C with the release of 114 J heat. Determine the specific heat of iron.

1. **Analyze the Problem**

   Known:

   energy released = **114 J**

   $\Delta T = $ **50.4°C – 25.0°C = 25.4°C**

   mass of iron = **10.0 g**

   Unknown:

   specific heat of iron = ?

2. **Solve for the Unknown**

   Write the equation for heat absorption.

   $$q = c \times m \times \Delta T$$

   Solve for c.

   $$q = \frac{c \times m \times \Delta T}{m \times \Delta T} \qquad c = \frac{q}{m \times \Delta T}$$

   $$c = \frac{114 \text{ J}}{(10.0 \text{ g})(25.4°\text{C})} = 0.449 \text{ J/(g·°C)}$$

3. **Evaluate the Answer**

   If the values used in the calculations have **three** significant figures, the answer must also have **three** significant figures. The calculated value matches the value for iron in Table 15.2.

REAL-WORLD CONNECTION
Describe two potential problems with the use of the Sun as a source of everyday energy.

1. <u>Weather conditions often reduce the available radiation.</u>

2. <u>Using photoelectric cells are costly.</u>

Energy and Chemical Change
Section 15.2 Heat

Main Idea	Details
	Skim *Section 2 of your text. Write three questions that come to mind from reading the headings and the illustration captions.*
	1. Accept all reasonable responses. Possible answers: Can a calorimeter measure the energy in food?
	2. Why is the calorimeter open to the environment?
	3. What is enthalpy?

New Vocabulary *Use your text to define each term.*

Main Idea	Details
calorimeter	an insulated device used for measuring the amount of heat absorbed or released during a chemical or physical process
thermochemistry	the study of heat changes that accompany chemical reactions and phase changes
system	in thermochemistry, the specific part of the universe containing the reaction or process being studied
surroundings	everything in the universe other than the system
universe	the system plus the surroundings
enthalpy	the heat content of a system at constant pressure
enthalpy (heat) of reaction	the change in enthalpy, or the heat absorbed or released, in a chemical reaction

Section 15.2 Heat (continued)

Main Idea	Details

Calorimetry

Use with page 523.

Describe *how a calorimeter measures heat.*

When a piece of hot metal is introduced into a cup of water, the

metal rod of the calorimeter absorbs heat from the water until both

the water and the rod have the same temperature.

Using Specific Heat

Use with Example Problem 15.3, page 525.

Summarize. *Fill in the blanks to help you take notes while you read Example Problem 15.3.*

• Problem

Determine the specific heat of a piece of metal with a mass of 4.68 g that **absorbs** 256 J of heat when its temperature increases by 182°C, and explain if the metal could be an **alkaline earth metal**.

1. Analyze the problem

Known: mass of metal = **4.68 g**

quantity of heat absorbed = **256 J**

ΔT = 182°C

Unknown: specific heat, c = ? J/(g · °C)

2. Solve for the Unknown

Write the equation for absorption of heat.

$q = $ **$c \times m \times \Delta T$**

Solve for c by dividing both sides of the equation by $m \times \Delta T$.

$$c = \frac{q}{m \times \Delta T}$$

Section 15.2 Heat (continued)

⟨Main Idea⟩ —— **⟨Details⟩** ————————————————

Substitute the known values into the equation.

$$c = \frac{256 \text{ J}}{(4.68 \text{ g})(182°C)} = \underline{0.301 \text{ J/(g} \cdot °C)}$$

Table 15.2 indicates the metal could be **strontium**.

3. Evaluate the Answer

The quantities used in the calculation have **three** significant figures, and the answer is correctly stated with **three** significant figures. The calculation yielded the **expected** unit, and the calculated **specific heat** is the same as that for **strontium**.

Chemical Energy and the Universe

Use with pages 525–528.

Compare and contrast *exothermic and endothermic reactions.*

In an exothermic reaction, energy is released. In an endothermic

reaction, energy is absorbed.

Write *the symbol for enthalpy (heat) of reaction.*

H_{rxn}

Explain *why chemists prefer to measure change in heat energy, rather than the total amount of heat energy present.*

It is impossible to know the total amount of heat energy present in a

substance because that depends on many factors, some of which

are not understood. It is possible to measure the heat absorbed or

lost by the object in a chemical reaction.

Energy and Chemical Change
Section 15.3 Thermochemical Equations

Main Idea ———

Details ———————————————————————

Skim *Section 3. Focus on the subheadings, boldfaced words, and the main ideas. In the space below, summarize the main idea of this section.*

The amount of energy absorbed by a system has the same numerical value

as the amount of energy released by the system, so that the enthalpy of

vaporization and condensation are the same but with different signs.

New Vocabulary *Use your text to define each term.*

thermochemical equation

a balanced chemical equation that includes the physical states of all

reactants and products and the energy change, usually expressed as

the change in enthalpy, ΔH

enthalpy (heat) of combustion

the enthalpy change for the complete burning of one mole of a substance

molar enthalpy (heat) of vaporization

the heat required to vaporize one mole of a liquid

molar enthalpy (heat) of fusion

the heat required to melt one mole of a solid substance

Section 15.3 Thermochemical Equations (continued)

Main Idea	Details
Writing Thermochemical Equations *Use with page 529.*	**Identify** *which of the reactions below is endothermic, and explain how you know.* 1. $4Fe(s) + 3O_2(g) \rightarrow 2Fe_2O_3(s)$ $\Delta H = -1625 \text{ kJ}$ 2. $NH_4NO_3(s) \rightarrow NH_4^+(aq) + NO_3^-(aq)$ $\Delta H = 27 \text{ kJ}$ Reaction 2 is endothermic. A positive value for ΔH indicates that energy was absorbed by the product; the enthalpy of the product is greater than the enthalpy of the reactant. **Identify** *which of the reactions below is exothermic, and explain how you know.* 1. $4Fe(s) + 3O_2(g) \rightarrow 2Fe_2O_3(s)$ $\Delta H = -1625 \text{ kJ}$ 2. $NH_4NO_3(s) \rightarrow NH_4^+(aq) + NO_3^-(aq)$ $\Delta H = 27 \text{kJ}$ Reaction 1 is exothermic. A negative value for ΔH indicates that energy was released by the product; the enthalpy of the product is less than the enthalpy of the reactant.
Changes of State *Use with pages 530–531.*	**Name** *the common states of matter.* solid, liquid, gas

Section 15.3 Thermochemical Equations (continued)

⟨Main Idea⟩ —————— **⟨Details⟩** ———————————————————————

Explain *changes in physical states by completing the sentences below.*

During vaporization, a __liquid__ becomes a __gas__.

Energy must be __absorbed__ by the liquid.

During condensation, a __gas__ becomes a __liquid__.

Energy is __released__ by the gas.

During fusion of ice, a __solid__ becomes a __liquid__.

Energy is __absorbed__ by the solid.

Identify *what the following equations represent.*

$\Delta H_{vap} = -\Delta H_{cond}$

The amount of energy absorbed during vaporization is numerically equal

to the amount of energy released during condensation.

$\Delta H_{fus} = -\Delta H_{solid}$

The amount of energy absorbed during fusion is numerically equal

to the amount of energy released during solidification.

REAL-WORLD CONNECTION Explain why a farmer would spray his orange trees with water when he knows the overnight temperature will be below 30°C.

As water freezes, it releases energy (ΔH_{fus}). This energy can increase the temperature of

the air enough to prevent frost damage to the oranges.

_____

Energy and Chemical Change
Section 15.4 Calculating Enthalpy Change

Main Idea ———

Details————————————————————

Scan *Section 4 of your text. Use the checklist below to preview the section.*

- Read all section titles.
- Read all boldfaced words.
- Read all tables and graphs.
- Look at all pictures and read the captions.
- Think about what you already know about energy and chemical change.

Write three statements about calculating enthalpy change based on your reading.

1. Accept all reasonable responses._____

2. _____

3. _____

New Vocabulary *Use your text to define each term.*

Hess's law

states that if you can add two or more thermochemical equations

to produce a final equation for a reaction, then the sum of the

enthalpy changes for the individual reactions is the enthalpy

change for the final reaction

standard enthalpy (heat) of formation

change in enthalpy that accompanies the formation of one mole of

the compound in its standard state from its constituent elements in

their standard states, written as ΔH_f^0

Section 15.4 Calculating Enthalpy Change (continued)

Main Idea	Details
Hess's Law *Use with pages 534–536.*	**Describe** *Hess's law by completing the following statement.* Hess's law is used to determine the **total enthalpy** of a system by imagining that each reaction is part of a **series of reactions**, each of which has a known ΔH. **Examine** *Figure 15.13. Read the caption and follow the arrows. Then apply Hess's law to fill in the blanks below.* ΔH for reaction **c** **−594 kJ** ΔH for reaction **d** **−198 kJ** sum of ΔH for reactions **c** and **d** **−792 kJ** In other words, the **enthalpy change** for the conversion of S and O_2 to SO_3 is **−792 kJ** .
Standard Enthalpy (Heat) of Formation *Use with pages 537–538.*	**Explain** *standard enthalpy of elements and compounds by completing the following statements.* An element's **standard state** is the normal **physical** state at one **atmosphere** pressure and **298 K**. For example, the standard state for iron is **solid**, for mercury is **liquid**, and for oxygen is **gas**. Free elements such as these are assigned a ΔH_f^0, or **standard enthalpy (heat) of formation**, of exactly **0.0 kJ**. The ΔH_f^0 of many **compounds** has been measured **experimentally**. For example, the standard enthalpies of formation for the following compounds are: $NO_2(g)$ **33** $SO_3(g)$ **−396** $SF_6(g)$ **−1220**

Section 15.4 Calculating Enthalpy Change (continued)

Main Idea	Details

The Summation Equation

Use with page 546.

Write *the formula that sums up the procedure for combining standard heats of formation equations to produce the desired equation and its* ΔH^0_{rxn}.

$$\Delta H^0_{rxn} = \Sigma\Delta H^0_f(\text{products}) - \Sigma\Delta H^0_f(\text{reactants})$$

This equation says to **subtract** the **sum** of heats of **formation** of the **reactants** from the sum of the **heats** of formation of the **products**.

Enthalpy Change from Standard Enthalpies of Formation

Use with Example Problem 15.6, page 540.

Summarize. *Fill in the blanks to help you take notes as you work through Example Problem 15.6.*

Problem ---·---·---·---·---·---·---·---·---·---·---·

Calculate ΔH^0_{rxn} for the combustion of methane.

$$CH_4(g) + 2O_2(g) \rightarrow CO_2(g) + 2H_2O(l)$$

1. Analyze the Problem

Use the formula $\Delta H^0_{rxn} = \Sigma\Delta H^0_f(\text{products}) - \Sigma\Delta H^0_f(\text{reactants})$ with data from Table R-11.

Known:

$\Delta H^0_f(CO_2) =$ __−394 kJ__

$\Delta H^0_f(H_2O) =$ __−286 kJ__

$\Delta H^0_f(CH_4) =$ __−75 kJ__

$\Delta H^0_f(O_2) =$ __0.0 kJ__

Unknown:

$\Delta H^0_{rxn} = ?$ kJ

Section 15.4 Calculating Enthalpy Change (continued)

Main Idea —— **Details** ————————————————————

2. Solve for the Unknown

Use the formula $\Delta H^O_{rxn} = \Sigma\Delta H^O_f$ (products) $- \Sigma\Delta H^O_f$ (reactants)

Substitute values in the formula

$\Delta H^O_{rxn} = \underline{[(-394\ kJ) + (2)(-286\ kJ)] - [(-75\ kJ) + (2)(0.0\ kJ)]}$

$\Delta H^O_{rxn} = \underline{[-966\ kJ] - [-75\ kJ]} = \underline{-891\ kJ}$

3. Evaluate the Answer

All values are <u>**correct**</u> to the stated place. The calculated value

matches that in Table R-11.

REAL-WORLD CONNECTION
Your family needs to choose a system to heat the new home you are building. From what you have learned so far, write down four questions you will use to evaluate the systems available. **Accept all reasonable responses. Possible answers:**

1. What is the most cost effective system? _____

2. How much heat is produced per quantity of each kind of fuel? _____

3. How will the heat be distributed? _____

4. What materials will the heating system be made of? _____

Energy and Chemical Change
Section 15.5 Reaction Spontaneity

Main Idea ———— **Details** ————————————————————

Scan *Section 5, using the checklist below as a guide.*

- Read all section titles.
- Read all boldfaced words.
- Read all tables and graphs.
- Look at all pictures and read the captions.
- Think about what you already know about energy and chemical change.

State *the main concepts of this section.*

Accept all reasonable responses. Possible answer: Spontaneous

processes occur with no outside intervention. Changes in entropy

and free energy determine the spontaneity of chemical reactions and

other processes.

New Vocabulary) *Use your text to define each term.*

spontaneous process **physical or chemical change that occurs with no outside intervention**

entropy **measure of the number of possible ways that the energy of a system**

can be distributed; this is related to the freedom of the system's

particles to move and number of ways they can be arranged.

second law of thermodynamics **states that spontaneous processes always proceed in such a way**

that entropy of the universe increases

free energy **energy that is available to do work**

Academic Vocabulary) *Define the following term.*

demonstrate **to show clearly**

Section 15.5 Reaction Spontaneity (continued)

Main Idea	Details
Spontaneous Processes	**Compare and contrast** *spontaneous processes and non-spontaneous processes.*
Use with pages 542–545.	Spontaneous processes occur without outside intervention. They may need some energy to start, but then they continue without additional help. For example, a match is used to ignite the gas for a stove's pilot light, but then the gas continues to burn on its own. Non-spontaneous processes cannot occur without outside intervention.

Identify *the parts of the entropy equation.*

$$\Delta S_{system} = S_{products} - S_{reactants}$$

ΔS represents the change in entropy of a system .

S represents the entropy of the system .

List *five reactions or processes in which it is possible to predict change in entropy. For each process, indicate whether entropy will increase or decrease.*

1. changes associated with a change in state (increase)

2. dissolving of a gas in a solvent (decrease)

3. number of gaseous product particles becomes greater than the number of gaseous reactant particles (increase)

4. solid or liquid dissolves to form a solution (increase)

5. temperature of a substance goes up (increase)

Section 15.5 Reaction Spontaneity (continued)

Main Idea	Details

Entropy, the Universe, and Free Energy

Use with pages 546–548.

Write *the equation for the standard free energy change under standard conditions.*

$\Delta G^0_{system} = \Delta H^0_{system} - T\Delta S^0_{system}$

Predict *whether entropy increases or decreases for the reaction below and explain your reasoning.*

$N_2(g) + 3H_2(g) \rightarrow 2NH_3(g)$

Entropy is negative because four moles of gas molecules react and only two moles of gas molecules are produced.

Describe *free energy changes by writing the word positive or negative in the appropriate blank.*

If the sign of the free energy change is **negative**, the reaction is spontaneous.

If the sign of the free energy system is **positive**, the reaction is non-spontaneous.

Explain *how ΔH^0_{system} and ΔS^0_{system} affect reaction spontaneity by completing the following table.*

How ΔH^0_{system} and ΔS^0_{system} Affect Reaction Spontaneity		
	$-\Delta H^0_{system}$	$+\Delta H^0_{system}$
$+\Delta S^0_{system}$	always spontaneous	spontaneity depends upon temperature
$-\Delta S^0_{system}$	spontaneity depends upon temperature	never spontaneous

Energy and Chemical Change Chapter Wrap-Up

*Now that you have read the chapter, review what you have learned
and write three key equations or relationships.*
Accept all reasonable responses. Possible answers:

1. $q = c \times m \times \Delta T$

2. The same amount of energy is absorbed in the melting of ice as is
   released in the freezing of water.

3. $\Delta H^0_{rxn} = \Sigma \Delta H^0_f \text{(products)} - \Sigma \Delta H^0_f \text{(reactants)}$

Review   *Use this checklist to help you study.*

☐ Study your Science Notebook for this chapter.

☐ Study the definitions of vocabulary words.

☐ Review daily homework assignments.

☐ Reread the chapter, reviewing the tables, graphs, and
  illustrations.

☐ Review the Section Assessment questions at the end of
  each section.

☐ Look over the Chapter Assessment at the end of the chapter.

REAL-WORLD CONNECTION

Explain why the energy that comes from
chemical reactions is critical for almost every phase of your daily life.

Accept all reasonable responses. Possible answer: The energy that comes from chemical

reactions makes most, if not all, of our daily activities possible. Chemical reactions are

involved in eating food, using household appliances, and riding in a car. We benefit from other

chemical reactions that manufacture the clothes we wear, the books we read, and more.

Reaction Rates

Before You Read

Define the following terms.

Boyle's law
states that the volume of a given amount of gas held at a constant

temperature varies inversely with the pressure

Charles's law
states that the volume of a given mass of gas is directly proportional

to its kelvin temperature at constant pressure

Gay-Lussac's law
states that the pressure of a given mass of gas varies directly with

the kelvin temperature when the volume remains constant

molarity
the number of moles of solute dissolved per liter of solution; also

known as molar concentration

Chapter 9 **Balance** *the following equation.*

$$\boxed{2}\ C_8H_{18}(l) + \boxed{25}\ O_2(g) \rightarrow \boxed{16}\ CO_2(g) + \boxed{18}\ H_2O(l)$$

Reaction Rates

Section 16.1 A Model for Reaction Rates

Main Idea ———— **Details** ——————————————————

Skim Section 1 of your text. Preview headings, photos, captions, boldfaced words, problems, and graphs. Write three questions that come to mind.

1. Accept all reasonable responses._____

2. _____

3. _____

New Vocabulary   *Use your text to define each term.*

reaction rate   the change in concentration of a reactant or product per unit of time,

expressed as moles per liter per second, or mol/(L·s)

collision theory   states that atoms, ions, and molecules must collide in order to react

activated complex   a temporary, unstable arrangement of atoms that may form products

or may break apart to re-form the reactants

activation energy   the minimum amount of energy that reacting particles must have to

form the activated complex and lead to a reaction

Academic Vocabulary   *Define the following term.*

investigate   to observe by study or close examination

Section 16.1 A Model for Reaction Rates (continued)

| Main Idea | Details |

Main Idea

Expressing Reaction Rates

Use with page 560.

Details

Identify *what each phrase or symbol represents in this equation.*

$$\text{Average rate} = \frac{\Delta \text{quantity}}{\Delta t}$$

Average rate = the average is used because the rate changes over time

$\Delta =$ <u>**a change in the quantity**</u>

$t =$ <u>**a specific period of time**</u>

Main Idea

Calculate Average Reaction Rates

Use with Example Problem 16.1, page 562.

Details

Summarize *Fill in the blanks to help you take notes while you read Example Problem 16.1.*

Problem —•

Calculate the average reaction rate of the chemical reaction using the <u>**change in concentration**</u> of butyl chloride in <u>**4.00 seconds**</u>.

1. **Analyze the Problem**

   Known: Unknown:

   <u>$t_1 = 0.00$ s</u>   **average reaction rate = ? mol/(L·s)**
   <u>$t_2 = 4.00$ s</u>

   $[C_4H_9Cl]$ at $t_1 = 0.220M$
   <u>$[C_4H_9Cl]$ at $t_2 = 0.100M$</u>

2. **Solve for the Unknown**
   Write the equation.

   $$\text{Average reaction rate} = -\frac{[C_4H_9Cl] \text{ at time } t_2 - [C_4H_9Cl] \text{ at time } t_1}{t_2 - t_1}$$

   Insert known quantities.

   Solve for the average rate $= -\dfrac{0.100M - 0.220M}{4.00 \text{ s} - 0.00 \text{ s}}$

   $= -\dfrac{-0.120 \text{ mol/L}}{4.00 \text{ s}}$

   Average reaction rate $=$ $\boxed{0.0300 \text{ mol/(L} \cdot \text{s)}}$

3. **Evaluate the Answer**

   The answer is correctly expressed in <u>**three**</u> significant figures.

Section 16.1 A Model for Reaction Rates (continued)

Main Idea ———— **Details** ——————————————————————————

Collision Theory

Use with pages 563–564.

Describe *how each of the items below affects a reaction.*

collision theory

Atoms, ions, and molecules must collide in order to react.

orientation and the activated complex

Atoms, ions, and molecules must collide with the correct orientation

in order to react and form the activated complex.

activation energy and reaction

Having a high-activation energy means that few collisions will have

the required energy for a reaction to occur, while having a low-

activation energy means more collisions and a higher reaction rate.

Analyze *Figure 16.4. Use colored pencils to draw similar molecules colliding. Be sure to include incorrect orientation, correct orientation, and correct orientation with insufficient energy. Develop a key for your drawings.*

Student drawings should be similar to Figure 16.4.

Use with page 565.

Explain *activation energy by completing the following paragraph.*

Some reactions have enough _energy_ to overcome the _activation_

energy of the reaction in order to form products. These are called

exothermic reactions. After the _activated complex_ is formed,

energy is released. In other reactions the reactants must absorb

energy to overcome the _activation energy_ of the reaction. These

reactions are called _endothermic reactions_.

REAL-WORLD CONNECTION

Describe how the collision theory would apply to a demolition derby.

The more cars that are participating, the greater the chance of a collision, and the faster the

cars are going, the greater the damage.

Reaction Rates

Section 16.2 Factors Affecting Reaction Rates

Main Idea	Details
	Scan *Section 2, using the checklist below as a guide.*
	• Read all section titles.
	• Read all boldfaced words.
	• Read all tables and graphs.
	• Look at all pictures and read the captions.
	• Think about what you already know about this topic.
	Write three facts you discovered about reaction rates.
	1. Accept all reasonable responses.
	2. _____
	3. _____

New Vocabulary — *Use your text to define each term.*

catalyst	a substance that increases the rate of a chemical reaction without itself being consumed in the reaction
inhibitor	a substance that slows down, or inhibits, reaction rates
heterogeneous catalyst	a catalyst that exists in a physical state different than that of the reaction it catalyzes
homogeneous catalyst	a catalyst that exists in the same physical state as the reaction it catalyzes

The Nature of Reactants

Use with page 568.

Explain *how reactants influence the rate at which a chemical reaction occurs by completing the following statement.*

As the reactant increases, the **reaction rate** increases.

Section 16.2 Factors Affecting Reaction Rates (continued)

Main Idea	Details
Use with pages 568–573.	**Explain** *the effect each of the following has on the rate of a reaction.*

reactivity of reactants

When the reactivity of the reactants increases, the reaction rate increases.

concentration

When the concentration of reactants increases, the reaction rate increases.

surface area

When the surface area increases, the reaction rate increases.

temperature

When the temperature is increased, the reaction rate increases.

catalyst

Catalysts increase the rate of a chemical reaction.

inhibitors

Inhibitors slow down the rate of a chemical reaction.

REAL-WORLD CONNECTION

Compare and contrast the rate at which a sugar cube in cold water and granulated sugar in warm water would dissolve. Include how surface area and the temperature of the water might affect the rate at which each dissolves. Create a statement about which would dissolve faster.

Granulated sugar in warm water would dissolve faster than the sugar cube in cold water. Both the

increase in surface area and the increase in temperature cause the rate of dissolving to increase.

Reaction Rates

Section 16.3 Reaction Rate Laws

Main Idea	Details
	Skim *Section 3 of your text. Choose a photograph from this section. Write a question based on what you see and read.*
	Accept all reasonable responses. Possible answer: How does a manometer measure pressure changes?

New Vocabulary *Use your text to define each term.*

rate law	the equation that expresses the mathematical relationship between the rate of a chemical reaction and the concentration of reactants
specific rate constant	the numerical value that relates reaction rate and concentration of reactants at a given temperature
reaction order	for a reactant, defines how the rate is affected by the concentration of that reactant
method of initial rates	determines reaction order by comparing the initial rates of a reaction carried out with varying reactant concentrations

Section 16.3 Reaction Rate Laws (continued)

Main Idea	Details

Writing Reaction Rate Laws

Use with pages 574–576.

Explain *what each symbol represents in the following equation.*
Rate = $k[A]$

$k =$ the specific rate constant, or a numerical value that relates

reaction rate and concentration of reactants at a given temperature

$[A] =$ the concentration of a reactant

Analyze *the rate law reaction for the decomposition of hydrogen peroxide.*
$$2H_2O_2 \longrightarrow 2H_2O + O_2$$

rate law equation: rate $= k[A]$, where $[A] =$ the reactant H_2O_2

insert the reactant: rate $= k[H_2O_2]$

Express *the rate law reaction for this chemical reaction.*
chemical equation: $2NO(g) + 2H_2(g) \longrightarrow N_2(g) + 2H_2O(g)$

rate law equation: rate $= k[A]^m[B]^n$, where $[A]$ represents

the reactant 2NO and $[B]$ represents the

reactant 2H$_2$

insert the reactants: rate $= k[NO]^2[H_2]$

Section 16.3 Reaction Rate Laws (continued)

⟨ **Main Idea** ⟩——— ⟨ **Details** ⟩————————————

Relate *how the reaction rate varies with:*

concentration

The reaction rate is directly proportional to the molar concentration

of reactant(s).

the overall reaction order

The reaction rate is directly proportional to the overall reaction

order, or the sum of the orders for the individual reactants.

**Determining
Reaction Order**

Use with page 576.

Explain *reaction order by completing the following sentences.*

One of the means of determining reaction order is by comparing

initial rates of a reaction with varying **reactant concentrations**.

This is known as the method of **initial rates**. This method requires

experimentation with differing **quantities** of the reactants and

comparing the **initial rate** of the reaction at each quantity. While

the rate law for a reaction can tell you the reaction rate, the rate

constant k, and the **concentration of the reactants**, actual **rate law**

and **order** of a complex reaction can be determined only through

experimentation.

┌───┐
│ **REAL-WORLD CONNECTION**   │
│   Consider whether an average of a │
│ student's grades on all chemistry tests is or is not a better way of determining a final │
│ grade as compared to using just one test score. Explain which is better and why. │
│   │
│ A given test score may be higher or lower than the student's usual performance. The average │
│   │
│ better reflects a student's overall understanding of the subject. │
└───┘

Reaction Rates

Section 16.4 Instantaneous Reaction Rates and Reaction Mechanisms

Main Idea ——— **Details** ————————————————

Skim *Section 4 of your text. Preview the headings, photos, captions, boldfaced words, problems, and graphs. Write three questions that come to mind.*

1. <u>Accept all reasonable responses.</u>

2. _____

3. _____

Use your text to define each term.

instantaneous rate <u>the slope of the straight line tangent to the curve at a specific time</u>

<u>in a chemical reaction</u>

complex reaction <u>a reaction that consists of two or more elementary steps</u>

reaction mechanism <u>the complete sequence of elementary steps that make up a complex</u>

<u>reaction</u>

intermediate <u>in a complex reaction, a substance produced in one elementary step</u>

<u>and consumed in a subsequent elementary step</u>

rate-determining step <u>the slowest of the elementary steps in a complex reaction</u>

Section 16.4 Instantaneous Reaction Rates and Reaction Mechanisms (continued)

Main Idea

Details

Calculate Instantaneous Reaction Rates

Use with Example Problem 16.2, page 579.

Summarize *Fill in the blanks to help you take notes while you read Example Problem 16.2.*

Problem

Calculate the instantaneous rate for this reaction, given the quantities for NO and H_2.

$$2NO(g) + H_2(g) \longrightarrow N_2O(g) + H_2O(g)$$

1. **Analyze the Problem**

   Known: Unknown:

   quantity of $[NO]$ = 0.00200M rate = ? mol/(L · s)

   quantity of $[H_2]$ = **0.00400M**

   k = **2.90 × 10^2 (L^2/(mol^2 · s))**

2. **Solve for the Unknown**

   Insert the known quantities into the rate law equation.

   rate = __$k[NO]^2[H_2]$__

   rate = __2.90 × 10^2 (L^2/(mol^2 · s)(0.00200 mol/L)^2(0.00400 mol/L)__

   rate = __4.64 × 10^{-6} mol/(L · s)__

3. **Evaluate the Answer**

   Are your units correct? Is your magnitude reasonable?

Reaction Mechanisms

Use with pages 580–582.

Compare *the reaction mechanism using the terms complex, intermediate, and rate-determining step to the process of building a car. Show that you understand the vocabulary.*

Building a car is complex. It is done on an assembly line in a series

of small steps. During the building process, some stages are slow

while others are fast. The rate-determining step compares to the

slowest building station. Each stage in the building process has

different materials that are incorporated into the car. These are like

the intermediates in a reaction.

Reaction Rates Chapter Wrap-Up

Now that you have read the chapter, list three facts you learned about reaction rates:

1. Accept all reasonable responses.

2. _____

3. _____

Review

Use this checklist to help you study.

☐ Study your Science Notebook for this chapter.

☐ Study the definitions of vocabulary words.

☐ Review daily homework assignments.

☐ Reread the chapter and review the tables, graphs, and illustrations.

☐ Review the Section Assessment questions at the end of each section.

☐ Look over the Chapter Assessment at the end of the chapter.

REAL-WORLD CONNECTION

Suppose you obtain a part-time job working for a lawn care business. Your new boss wants you to help her choose the right fertilizer for most of the lawns you will see. Use the terms from this chapter to explain to your boss what she should look for in a fertilizer.

The fertilizer should work over a large surface area for increased solubility, be of the right

concentration for proper use, and work within the range of temperatures likely to be

experienced in the area that you service.

Chemical Equilibrium

Before You Read

Review Vocabulary *Define the following terms.*

chemical equation   a statement using chemical formulas to describe the identities and

relative amounts of the reactants and products involved in a

chemical reaction

reaction rate   the change in concentration of a reactant or product per unit of time,

expressed as moles per liter per second, or mol/(L · s)

rate law   the mathematical relationship between the rate of a chemical

reaction at a given temperature and the concentrations of

reactants

Chapter 9   **Balance** *the chemical equation below.*

$$NO(g) + H_2(g) \qquad\qquad N_2O(g) + H_2O(g)$$

$$2NO(g) + H_2(g) \longrightarrow N_2O(g) + H_2O(g)$$

Chapter 16   **Write** *the rate law for the reaction below.*

$$H_2(g) + I_2(g) \longrightarrow 2\,HI(g)$$

Rate = $k[H_2][I_2]$

Chemical Equilibrium

Section 17.1 A State of Dynamic Balance

(Main Idea) ——————   **(Details)** ——————————————————————————

Skim *Section 1 of your text. Write a statement that describes the nature of equilibrium from your reading of the headings, boldface terms, and illustration captions.*

Accept all reasonable responses.

_____

_____

_____

New Vocabulary   *Use your text to define each term.*

reversible reaction   **a reaction that can occur in both the forward and the reverse directions**

chemical equilibrium   **a state in which the forward and reverse reactions balance each other**

because they take place at equal rates

law of chemical equilibrium   **states that at a given temperature, a chemical system may reach a**

state in which a particular ratio of reactant and product

concentrations has a constant value

equilibrium constant   **the ratio of product concentrations to reactant concentrations,**

with each raised to the power equal to its coefficient in the balanced

equation (K_{eq})

homogeneous equilibrium   **a state of equilibrium in which all the reactants and products are in**

the same physical state

heterogeneous equilibrium   **a state of equilibrium in which the reactants and products of a**

reaction are present in more than one physical state

Section 17.1 A State of Dynamic Balance (continued)

Main Idea	Details

What is equilibrium?

Use with pages 594–598.

Explain *reversible reactions by inserting the words left and right in the following statements.*

The reactants for the forward reaction are on the __left__ . The products are on the __right__ . The reactants for the reverse reaction are on the __right__ . The products are on the __left__ .

List *the reactants and products of the following reversible reaction.*

$N_2(g) + 3H_2(g) \rightleftharpoons 2NH_3(g)$

	Reactants	Products
Forward reaction	N_2 H_2	NH_3
Reverse reaction	NH_3	N_2 H_2

Complete *the following statement.*

The state in which forward and reverse reactions balance each other because they take place at equal rates is called __chemical__ __equilibrium__ . Although a chemical reaction may be in equilibrium, the __products__ and __reactants__ may continually be __changing__ because chemical equilibrium is a dynamic process.

Equilibrium Expressions and Constants

Use with pages 599–604.

Identify *the parts of the equilibrium constant expression.*

$$K_{eq} = \frac{[C]^c[D]^d}{[A]^a[B]^b}$$

K_{eq}	=	the equilibrium constant
$[C][D]$	=	the products
$[A][B]$	=	the reactants
a, b, c, and d	=	the coefficients in the balanced equation

Section 17.1 A State of Dynamic Balance (continued)

Main Idea	Details

Write *the equilibrium constant expression for the following balanced chemical equation.*

$$N_2(g) + 3H_2(g) \rightleftharpoons 2NH_3(g)$$

$$K_{eq} = \frac{[NH_3]^2}{[N_2][H_2]^3}$$

Compare and contrast *homogeneous equilibrium and hetero-geneous equilibrium by completing the following sentences.*

Homogeneous equilibrium occurs when __reactants__ and __products__ of a reaction are in the __same__ physical state. Heterogeneous equilibrium occurs when __reactants__ and __products__ of a reaction are in more than __one__ physical state. Equilibrium depends on the __concentration of gases__ in the system.

Write *the equilibrium expression for this reaction.*

$$I_2(s) \rightleftharpoons I_2(g)$$

$$K_{eq} = [I_2(g)]$$

REAL-WORLD CONNECTION Discuss why sodium hydrogen carbonate is valuable in baking.

Decomposition releases carbon dioxide gas that gets trapped in dough. The dough rises during cooking due to expansion of the hot gas.

Section 17.1 A State of Dynamic Balance (continued)

<table>
<tr><td>

Main Idea

The Value of Equilibrium Constants

Use with Example Problem 17.3, page 605.

</td><td>

Details

Summarize *Fill in the blanks to help you take notes while you read Example Problem 17.3.*

Problem ──────────────────────────────────

Calculate the value of K_{eq} for the equilibrium constant expression.

$$K_{eq} = \frac{[NH_3]^2}{[N_2][H_2]^3}$$

1. Analyze the Problem

List the knowns and unknowns.

Known: the equilibrium constant expression:

$$K_{eq} = \frac{[NH_3]^2}{[N_2][H_2]^3}$$

_____

Known: the concentration of each reactant and product:

$[NH_3] = $ **0.933 mol/L** _____

$[N_2] \quad = $ **0.533 mol/L** _____

$[H_2] \quad = $ **1.600 mol/L** _____

Unknown: the value of the equilbrium constant

2. Solve for the Unknown

Substitute the ____**known values**____ into the equilibrium

____**constant expression**____ and calculate its value.

$$K_{eq} = \frac{[0.933]^2}{[0.533][1.600]^3} = \underline{\quad 0.399 \quad}$$

3. Evaluate the Answer

The given concentrations have __**3**__ significant figures, therefore

the answer must have __**3**__ significant figures.

</td></tr>
</table>

Chemical Equilibrium

Section 17.2 Factors Affecting Chemical Equilibrium

Main Idea ————

Details ————————————————————

Scan *Section 2 of your text. Use the checklist below as a guide.*

- Read all section titles.
- Read all boldfaced words.
- Read all tables and graphs.
- Look at all figures and read the captions.
- Think about what you already know about chemical equilibrium.

Write *four facts you discovered about chemical equilibrium.*

1. Accept all reasonable responses._____

2. _____

3. _____

4. _____

New Vocabulary   *Use your text to define the following term.*

Le Châtelier's principle   states that if a stress is applied to a system at equilibrium, the system

shifts in the direction that relieves the stress

Section 17.2 Factors Affecting Chemical Equilibrium (continued)

Main Idea	Details
Applying Le Châtelier's Principle *Use with pages 607–610.*	**Determine** *how each of the following changes affects a system in equilibrium. Write a sentence that includes the term(s) in parentheses.* changes in concentration (collisions) **Increasing the concentration increases the number of effective collisions.** changes in volume (pressure, products) **Decreasing volume increases pressure. To relieve the stress, more products are formed.** changes in temperature (endothermic, exothermic) **If heat is added, the reaction shifts toward the direction that uses up the heat. When heat is a product, the reaction is exothermic. When heat is a reactant, the reaction is endothermic.**

REAL-WORLD CONNECTION

Describe how your body would relieve the stress placed on it by climbing to a high altitude.

High altitudes have less oxygen. The body produces more hemoglobin to carry the available

oxygen.

_____

Chemical Equilibrium

Section 17.3 Using Equilibrium Constants

Main Idea ——— **Details** ———————————————

Scan *Section 3 of your text. Use the checklist below as a guide.*

- Read all section heads.
- Read all boldfaced words.
- Read all the tables and graphs.
- Look at all pictures and read the captions.
- Think about what you already know about equilibrium constants.

Write *three facts you discovered about using equilibrium constants.*

1. Accept all reasonable responses._____

2. _____

3. _____

New Vocabulary *Use your text to define each term.*

solubility product constant   an equilibrium constant expression for the dissolving of a sparingly

soluble ionic compound in water

common ion   an ion that is common to two or more ionic compounds

common ion effect   the lowering of the solubility of a substance by the presence of a

common ion

Section 17.3 Using Equilibrium Constants (continued)

Main Idea ————

Calculating Equilibrium Concentrations

Use with Example Problem 17.4, page 613.

Details ————————————————————

Summarize *Fill in the blanks to help you take notes while you read example Problem 17.4.*

Problem ----------------------------------

At 1405 K, hydrogen sulfide <u>**decomposes**</u> to form <u>**hydrogen**</u> and a diatomic <u>**sulfur**</u> molecule, S_2. The <u>**equilibrium constant**</u> for the reaction is 2.27×10^{-3}.

$$2H_2S(g) \rightleftharpoons 2H_2(g) + S_2(g)$$

What is the concentration of $H_2(g)$ if $[S_2] = 0.0540$ mol/L and $[H_2S] = 0.184$ mol/L?

1. **Analyze the Problem**

   List the knowns and unknowns.

   Known: Unknown:

   K_{eq} = ___**2.27 × 10⁻³**___ $[H_2]$ = ___**? mol/L**___

   $[S_2]$ = ___**0.0540 mol/L**___

   $[H_2S]$ = ___**0.184 mol/L**___

2. **Solve for the Unknown**

   Write the equilibrium constant expression.

   $$K_{eq} = \frac{[H_2]^2[S_2]}{[H_2S]^2}$$

   Substitute known quantities.

   $$2.27 \times 10^{-3} = \frac{[H_2]^2 (0.0540)}{(0.184)^2}$$

   Solve for the unknown.

   $$[H_2]^2 = 2.27 \times 10^{-3} \times \frac{(0.184)^2}{(0.0540)} = 1.42 \times 10^{-3}$$

   $$[H_2] = \sqrt{1.42 \times 10^{-3}} = 0.0377 \text{ mol/L}$$

3. **Evaluate the Answer**

   The number of significant figures in the data is <u>**three**</u>. Therefore, the number of significant figures in the answer must be <u>**three**</u>.

Section 17.3 Using Equilibrium Constants (continued)

Main Idea ——— **Details** ———————————————————

The Solubility Product Constant

Use with pages 614–619.

Describe *solubility equilibrium.*

The rate of the forward reaction is equal to the rate of the reverse reaction.

Identify *the part of the equation that shows equilibrium and circle it.*

$$BaSO_4(s) \;\overline{\underline{\Longleftrightarrow}}\; Ba^{2+}(aq) + SO_4^{2-}(aq)$$

Explain *solubility by completing the following statements.*

<u>Solubility</u> is the amount of a substance that will <u>dissolve</u> in a given volume of <u>water</u> .

K_{sp} represents the <u>solubility product constant</u> .

K_{sp} is the <u>product</u> of the concentration <u>of ions</u> each raised to the power equal to the <u>coefficient</u> of the ion in the <u>chemical equation</u> .

K_{sp} depends only on the <u>concentrations</u> of the <u>ions</u> in a saturated <u>solution</u> .

Explain *why it benefits doctors to understand solubility.*

The relative solubility of medicines determines if they can be used.

Calculating Molar Solubility

Use with Example Problem 17.5, page 616.

Summarize *Fill in the blanks to help you take notes while you read Example Problem 17.5.*

• **Problem** --•

Calculate the solubility in mol/L of copper(II) carbonate ($CuCO_3$) at 298 K.

1. **Analyze the Problem**
   List the knowns and unknowns.

   Known: Unknown:

   K_{sp} ($CuCO_3$) = <u>**2.5 × 10^{-10}**</u>   solubility ($CuCO_3$) = <u>**? mol/L**</u>

Section 17.3 Using Equilibrium Constants (continued)

Main Idea	Details

2. Solve for the Unknown

Write the balanced chemical equation.

$$CuCO_3(s) \rightleftharpoons Cu^{2+}(aq) + CO_3^{2-}(aq)$$

Write the solubility constant expression (remember only the ions are used).

$$K_{sp} = [Cu^{2+}][CO_3^{2-}] = 2.5 \times 10^{-10}$$

$$s = [Cu^{2+}] = [CO_3^{2-}]$$

Substitute s for $[Cu^2+]$ and $[CO_3^{2-}]$

$$(s)(s) = s^2 = 2.5 \times 10^{-10}$$

$$s = \sqrt{2.5 \times 10^{-10}} = 1.6 \times 10^{-5} \text{ mol/L}$$

3. Evaluate the Answer

K_{sp} has __2__ significant figures so the answer must be expressed with __2__ significant figures.

Describe *conditions in which precipitates are likely to form.*

1. the K_{sp} constant is a very small number

2. if one of the products of a reaction has low solubility

3. if adding an ionic compound with a common ion shifts the

solubility equilibrium to the left

The Common Ion Effect

Use with pages 620–621.

Discuss *the common ion effect by completing the following paragraph.*

An ion that is common to two or more ionic compounds is known as a __common ion__. The lowering of the solubility of a substance by the presence of a common ion is called the __common ion effect__ .

Chemical Equilibrium Chapter Wrap-Up

Now that you have read the chapter, review what you have learned.

Describe *chemical equilibrium.*

a reaction in which the forward and reverse reactions occur at equal

rates and the concentration of reactants and products remains

constant

Explain *Le Châtelier's principle.*

describes how an equilibrium system shifts in response to a stress

_____

Review

Use this checklist to help you study.

☐ Study your Science Notebook for this chapter.

☐ Study the vocabulary words and scientific definitions.

☐ Review daily homework assignments.

☐ Reread the chapter and review the tables, graphs, and illustrations.

☐ Review the Section Assessment questions at the end of each section.

☐ Look over the Study Guide at the end of the chapter.

REAL-WORLD CONNECTION Describe several uses of solubility in your home.

Accept all reasonable answers._____

_____

_____

Acids and Bases

Before You Read

Define the following term.

chemical equilibrium | a state in which forward and reverse reactions balance each other

because they occur at equal rates

Chapter 9

Write *the equation for hydrogen chloride dissolving in water to form hydrogen ions and chloride ions.*

$HCl(g) \rightarrow H^+(aq) + Cl^-(aq)$

Explain *what type of compound hydrogen chloride is since it produces hydrogen ions in aqueous solution.*

The compound is an acid.

Chapter 16

Identify *five factors that influence reaction rate.*

1. the reactive nature of the reactants

2. the concentrations of the reacting particles

3. surface area

4. temperature

5. adding a catalyst

Acids and Bases

Section 18.1 Introduction to Acids and Bases

(Main Idea) ─────── **(Details)** ───────────────────────────

Skim *Section 1 of your text. Write two questions that come to mind from reading the headings and the illustration captions.*

1. Accept all reasonable responses.

2. _____

(New Vocabulary) *Use your text to define each term.*

acidic solution	a solution that contains more hydrogen ions than hydroxide ions
basic solution	a solution that contains more hydroxide ions that hydrogen ions
Arrhenius model	an acid-base model that states that an acid is a substance that contains hydrogen and ionizes to produce hydrogen ions in aqueous solution, and that a base is a substance that contains a hydroxide group and dissociates to produce a hydroxide ion in aqueous solution
Brønsted-Lowry model	an acid-base model in which an acid is a hydrogen-ion donor and a base is a hydrogen-ion acceptor
conjugate acid	the species produced when a base accepts a hydrogen ion from an acid
conjugate base	the species that results when an acid donates a hydrogen ion to a base
conjugate acid-base pair	two substances related to each other by the donating and accepting of a single hydrogen ion
amphoteric	substances that can act as both acids and bases
Lewis model	an acid-base model in which a Lewis acid is an electron-pair acceptor and a Lewis base is an electron-pair donor

Section 18.1 Introduction to Acids and Bases (continued)

Main Idea	Details

Properties of Acids and Bases

Use with pages 634–636.

Compare and contrast *the properties of an acid and a base by placing an X in the Acid column if the property applies to an acid and in the Base column if the property applies to a base.*

Acid	Properties	Base
X	tastes sour	
	tastes bitter	X
	feels slippery	X
X	affects color	X
X	reacts with metal	
X	conducts electricity	X
X	has more hydrogen ions than hydroxide ions	
	has more hydroxide ions than hydrogen ions	X

Write *the chemical equation for the self-ionization of water.*

$$H_2O(l) + H_2O(l) \rightleftharpoons H_3O^+(aq) + OH^-(aq)$$

The Arrhenius and Brønsted-Lowry Models

Use with pages 637–639.

Analyze *why the Arrhenius model of acids and bases does NOT include ammonia (NH₃) in solution as a base.*

Because ammonia does not include OH⁻ (a hydroxide ion), ammonia

does not fit the Arrhenius definition of a base, which says that a base

contains a hydroxide group.

Identify *which of the following statements describes the Arrhenius model and which describes the Brønsted-Lowry model by filling in the blanks.*

The Arrhenius model is based on the dissociation of compounds, while the Brønsted-Lowry model is based on the donation and acceptance of hydrogen ions. Conjugate acid-base pairs are a component of the Brønsted-Lowry model and are NOT a component of the Arrhenius model.

Section 18.1 Introduction to Acids and Bases (continued)

Main Idea ———— **Details** ————————————————————

Describe *what happens in the forward and reverse reactions when ammonia is dissolved in water. Identify the conjugate acid, the conjugate base, and the two conjugate acid-base pairs.*

In the forward reaction, water is a Brønsted–Lowry acid because it gives up a H^+

ion. Ammonia is a Brønsted-Lowry base because the NH_3 molecule accepts a

H^+ ion to form the ammonium ion NH_4^+. In the reverse reaction, the ammonium

ion gives up a H^+ ion to form the molecule ammonia and acts as a Brønsted-

Lowry acid, and the hydroxide ion donated by the water is a Brønsted-Lowry

base because it accepts a H^+ ion to form a water molecule. The ammonium ion

is the conjugate acid of the base ammonia. The ammonia and the ammonium

ion are a conjugate acid-base pair. The hydroxide ion is the conjugate base of

the acid water. The water and the hydroxide ion are a conjugate acid-base pair.

Monoprotic and Polyprotic Acids

Use with pages 640–641.

Explain *what a polyprotic acid is.*

A polyprotic acid is any acid that has more than one ionizable hydrogen atom.

Sequence *the following equations in the steps of the ionization of phosphoric acid in the correct order.*

___3___ $HPO_4^{2-}(aq) + H_2O(l) \rightleftharpoons H_3O^+(aq) + PO_4^{3-}(aq)$

___1___ $H_3PO_4(aq) + H_2O(l) \rightleftharpoons H_3O^+(aq) + H_2PO_4^{2-}(aq)$

___2___ $H_2PO_4^-(aq) + H_2O(l) \rightleftharpoons H_3O^+(aq) + HPO_4^-(aq)$

The Lewis Model

Use with pages 641–643.

Define and give examples of an anhydride, distinguishing between those that produce an acid and those that produce a base.

An anhydride is an oxide that can become an acid or base by adding the

elements contained in water. Oxides of nonmetallic elements, such as carbon,

sulfur, and nitrogen, produce an acid in aqueous solution. Oxides of metallic

elements, such as calcium oxide, usually form basic solutions.

Acids and Bases
Section 18.2 Strengths of Acids and Bases

Main Idea ————— **Details** ——————————————

Skim *Section 2 of your text. Focus on the headings, subheadings, boldfaced words, and the main ideas. Write three questions about strengths of acids and basis based on what you have read.*

1. Accept all reasonable responses._____

2. _____

3. _____

New Vocabulary *Use your text to define each term.*

strong acid   an acid that ionizes completely

weak acid   an acid that ionizes only partially in dilute aqueous solution

acid ionization constant   the value of the equilibrium constant expression for the ionization of

a weak acid

strong base   a base that dissociates entirely into metal ions and hydroxide ions

weak base   a base that ionizes only partially in dilute aqueous solution to form

the conjugate acid of the base and hydroxide ion

base ionization constant   the value of the equilibrium constant expression for the ionization

of a base

Section 18.2 Strengths of Acids and Bases (continued)

Main Idea	Details

Strengths of Acids

Use with pages 644–647.

Explain *why all acids are not equal in strength.*

Some acids ionize completely, which makes them strong, and other

acids do not ionize completely, which makes them weak.

Identify *the acids in the following table as strong or weak.*

Acid	Strong or Weak	Acid	Strong or Weak
acetic	**weak**	hydroiodic	**strong**
carbonic	**weak**	hydrosulfuric	**weak**
		hypochlorous	**weak**
hydrochloric	**strong**	nitric	**strong**
hydrofluoric	**weak**	sulfuric	**strong**

Describe *the difference in conductivity between strong and weak acids.*

Because ions carry electricity through a solution, strong acids produce

the maximum number of ions, and they are good conductors of electricity.

Weak acids have fewer ions and, as a result, do not conduct electricity as

well as strong acids do.

Analyze *equilibrium constant expressions by completing the following statements.*

The concentration of liquid water in the denominator of an equilibrium constant expression is considered to be **constant** in dilute aqueous solutions. Therefore, liquid water can be **combined with** K_{eq} to give a new equilibrium constant, K_a. For weak acids, the equilibrium **concentration** of the **products** in the numerator tends to be small compared to the equilibrium **concentration** of the **reactants** in the denominator. The weakest acids have the **smallest** K_a values because their solutions have the highest concentrations of **un-ionized** acid molecules.

Section 18.2 Strengths of Acids and Bases (continued)

⟨Main Idea⟩ ——————— ⟨Details⟩ ————————————————————————————

Strengths of Bases

Use with pages 648 and 649.

Compare and contrast *the strengths of acids and bases by completing this concept map using the terms ionize, ionization constant, strong, stronger, weak, and weaker.*

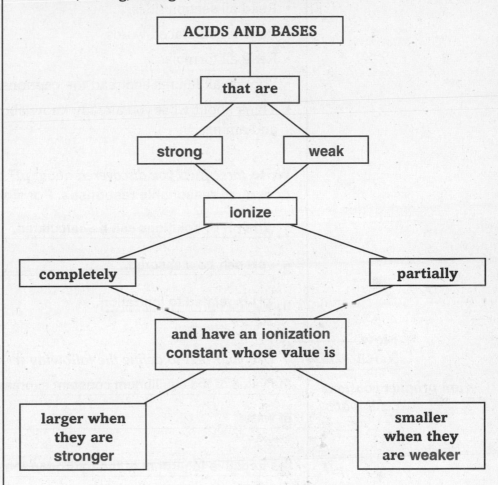

Describe *the differences between the strength and the concentration of acids and bases by completing the following statements.*

The number of the acid or base molecules dissolved is described by the terms **dilute** and **concentrated**. The degree to which an acid or base separates into ions is described by the terms **weak** and **strong**. A strong acid can be a **dilute** solution and a **weak** acid can be a concentrated solution.

Acids and Bases

Section 18.3 Hydrogen Ions and pH

Main Idea	**Details**
	Scan *Section 3 of your text. Use the checklist below as a guide.*
	• Read all section titles.
	• Read all boldfaced words.
	• Read all formulas.
	• Look at all figures and read the captions.
	• Think about what you already know about alcohols, ethers, and amines.
	Write *three facts you discovered about pH as you scanned the section.* **Accept all reasonable responses. Possible answers:**
	1. The pH of solutions can be calculated.
	2. pH can be measured.
	3. pH is related to ionization.

New Vocabulary	*Use your text to define the following terms.*
ion product constant for water	the value of the equilibrium constant expression for the self-ionization of water
pH	the negative logarithm of the hydrogen ion concentration
pOH	the negative logarithm of the hydroxide ion concentration

Section 18.3 Hydrogen Ions and pH (continued)

Main Idea	Details

Ion Product Constant for Water

Use with pages 650–651.

Describe *how the ion product constant for water is derived from the self-ionization equation.*

$$H_2O(l) \rightleftharpoons H^+(aq) + OH^-(aq)$$

$$K_{eq} = [H^+][OH^-] / [H_2O]$$

$$K_{eq}[H_2O] = K_w = [H^+][OH^-]$$

$$K_w = [H^+][OH^-] = (1.0 \times 10^{-7})(1.0 \times 10^{-7}) = 1.0 \times 10^{-14}$$

Calculate $[H^+]$ and $[OH^-]$ Using K_w

Use with Example Problem 18.1, page 651.

Summarize *Fill in the blanks to help you take notes while you read Example Problem 18.1.*

Problem

Calculate $[OH^-]$ using __K_w__ and the concentration of __$[H^+]$__, and determine if the solution is acidic, basic, or neutral.

Step 1: Analyze the Problem

Known: Unknown:

$[H^+] = $ __1.0×10^{-5} *M*__ $[OH^-] = ?$ mol/L

$K_w = $ __1.0×10^{-14}__

Write what you can predict about $[OH^-]$:

__$[OH^-]$ will be less than 1.0×10^{-7}__

Step 2: Solve for the Unknown

Write the ion product constant expression

$K_w = $ __$[H^+][OH^-] = 1.0 \times 10^{-14}$__

Solve for $[OH^-]$ by __dividing both sides of the equation by $[H^+]$__.

$[OH^-] = $ __$K_w/[H^+]$__

$[OH^-] = $ __$(1.0 \times 10^{-14})/(1.0 \times 10^{-5}) = 1.0 \times 10^{-9}$ mol/L__

Since $[H^+] > [OH^-]$, __the solution is acidic__.

Section 18.3 Hydrogen Ions and pH (continued)

Main Idea —— **Details** _____

> **Step 3: Evaluate the Answer**
>
> The answer is correctly stated with <u>two</u> significant figures because [H$^+$] and [OH$^-$] each have two. The hydroxide ion concentration <u>matched</u> the prediction.

pH and pOH

Use with pages 652–658.

Compare and contrast *pH and pOH by completing the following table.*

Solution Type	Scale Measure	Relationship (Equation)
acid	pH	pH = $-\log$[H$^+$]
base	pOH	pOH = $-\log$[OH$^-$]
acid and base	pH + pOH	pH + pOH = 14.00

Analyze *the process of calculating pH and pOH from the hydroxide concentration.*

Calculate the pOH from concentration of the hydroxide. This is done

by calculating the negative log of the concentration. Then subtract

the pOH value from 14 to find the pH value.

Describe *the process of calculating the hydrogen ion and hydroxide ion concentrations from pH.*

First find the concentration of the hydrogen ion by calculating the

antilog of the negative pH. Then subtract the pH value from 14 to

find the pOH value.

Describe *the process of calculating* K$_a$ *from pH for a 0.100M weak acid.*

Set up the acid ionization constant expression for this acid. Then use pH to find the

hydrogen ion concentration. We know that the number of hydrogen ions must be equal to

the conjugate base concentration in an ionization reaction. Therefore, the weak acid

concentration must equal the 0.100 molar concentration minus the hydrogen ion

concentration. Last, substitute the concentrations in the K$_a$ expression and solve.

Acids and Bases
Section 18.4 Neutralization

Main Idea ——————— **Details** ————————————————

Skim *Section 4 of your text. Focus on the headings, subheadings, boldfaced words, and the main ideas. Write three questions about strengths of acids and basis based on what you have read.*

1. **Accept all reasonable responses.** _____

2. _____

3. _____

New Vocabulary 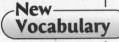 *Define the following terms.*

neutralization reaction
reaction in which an acid and a base in aqueous solution react to

produce a salt and water; it is a double-replacement reaction

salt
an ionic compound made up of a cation from a base and an anion from an acid

titration
a stoichiometric method for determining the concentration of a solution by

reacting a known volume of the solution with a solution of known concentration

titrant
a titrating solution of known concentration, called the standard solution

equivalence point
point at which moles of hydrogen ions from the acid equal moles of the

hydroxide ions from the base; the stoichiometric ratio is equivalent

acid-base indicator
chemical dyes whose colors are affected by acidic and basic solutions

end point
the point at which the indicator used in a titration changes color

because the equivalence point is reached

salt hydrolysis
process in which anions of the dissociated salt accept hydrogen ions from

water or the cations of the dissociated salt donate hydrogen ions to water

buffer
solution that resists changes in pH when limited amounts of acid or base are added

buffer capacity
the amount of acid or base a buffer solution can absorb without a

significant change in pH

Section 18.4 Neutralization (continued)

Main Idea —— **Details** —————————————

Reactions Between Acids and Bases

Use with pages 659–664.

Write *the full equation of the neutralization reaction for magnesium hydroxide and hydrochloric acid.*

$Mg(OH)_2(aq) + 2HCl(aq) \rightarrow MgCl_2(aq) + 2H_2O(l)$

Draw *the titration curve for 50.0 mL 0.100M HCl titrated with 0.100M NaOH. Label the pH and volume vectors, as well as the equivalence point.*

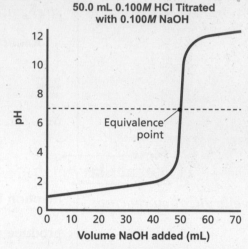

50.0 mL 0.100*M* HCl Titrated with 0.100*M* NaOH

Describe *the indicator that matches each of the following pH levels. Use Figure 18.24 as a guide.*

pH	Indicator
7.2	phenol red
4.2	methyl orange
1.8	cresol red
1–12	universal indicator

Explain *the process for calculating the molarity of an unknown HCOOH solution by completing the equations below.*

Balanced equation:

$HCOOH(aq) + NaOH(aq) \rightarrow HCOONa(aq) + H_2O(l)$

18.28 mL NaOH × **1 L NaOH/1000 mL NaOH** = **0.01828** L NaOH

0.01828 L NaOH × **0.1000 mol NaOH/1 L NaOH**

= **1.828×10^{-3}** mol NaOH

1.828×10^{-3} mol NaOH × **1 mol HCOOH /1 mol NaOH**

= **1.828×10^{-3}** mol HCOOH

1.828×10^{-3} mol HCOOH /**0.02500 L HCOOH**

= **7.312×10^{-2}** *M* HCOOH

Section 18.4 Neutralization (continued)

Main Idea ————— **Details** —————————————————

Salt Hydrolysis

Use with page 665.

Describe *salt hydrolysis by completing the following statements.*

Some aqueous salt solutions are neutral, some are basic, and some are **acidic** . The reason for this is a process known as **salt hydrolysis**. In this process, the anions of the dissociated salt donate **hydrogen ions** to water. Salts that will hydrolyze have a weak acid and a **strong base** or a strong acid and a **weak base** . A salt formed from a strong acid and a weak base will form an **acidic solution** . A salt formed from a strong base and a weak acid will form a **basic solution** . Salts formed from weak acids and bases or from strong acids and bases will not hydrolyze and form **neutral solutions** .

Buffered Solutions

Use with pages 666–667.

Explain *how a buffer works by completing the table below.*

The equation at equilibrium	$HF(aq) \rightleftharpoons H^+(aq) + F^-(aq)$	
Δ Condition	Equilibrium Shift	The Process
add acid	left	The H^+ ions react with F^- ions to form **additional HF molecules.**
add base	right	The OH^- ions react with H^+ ions to form water. This decreases the concentration of the H^+ ions so that **more H^+ ions need to be made.**
A greater **concentration** of the buffering molecules and ions in the solution leads to a **greater buffering capacity** of the solution.		
A buffer has **equal quantities** of an acid and its **conjugate base** or a base with its **conjugate acid.**		

Acids and Bases Chapter Wrap-Up

Now that you have read the chapter, review what you have learned; write out three key equations and relationships.
Accept all reasonable responses. Possible answers:

1. <u>A strong acid has a weak conjugate base, and a weak acid has a strong conjugate base.</u>

2. <u>$K_w = 1.0 \times 10^{-14}$</u>

3. <u>pH + pOH = 14.00</u>

Review | *Use this checklist to help you study.*

☐ Study your Science Notebook for this chapter.

☐ Study the definitions of vocabulary words.

☐ Review daily homework assignments.

☐ Reread the chapter and review the tables, graphs, and illustrations.

☐ Review the Section Assessment questions at the end of each section.

☐ Look over the Study Guide at the end of the chapter.

REAL-WORLD CONNECTION

Suppose you are on the bench for your school's soccer team when one of the players comes out of the game with a cramp. A teammate suggests that she start breathing into a paper bag to recover sooner. Explain whether or not this is good advice.

<u>It is not good advice, as the cramping may be caused by acidosis, or a lowering of pH in the</u>

<u>blood due to excessive acid levels. Breathing into a paper bag will cause the soccer player to</u>

<u>inhale more CO_2 which could further lower pH levels, making the condition worse.</u>

Redox Reactions

Before You Read

Define the following terms.

electronegativity

indicates the relative ability of an element's atoms to attract

electrons in a chemical bond

chemical reactions

processes by which the atoms of one or more substances are

rearranged to form different substances; a chemical change

Chapter 7

Compare and contrast *monatomic ions and polyatomic ions.*

Monatomic ions are ions formed from only one atom. Polyatomic

Ions are ions made up of two or more atoms bonded together that

act as a single unit with a net charge.

Chapter 9

List *five types of chemical reactions.*

1. synthesis

2. combustion

3. decomposition

4. single-replacement

5. double-replacement

Redox Reactions

Section 19.1 Oxidation and Reduction

Main Idea ——— ## Details ——————————————

Skim *Section 1 of your text. Write three questions that come to mind from reading the headings and the illustration captions.*

1. Accept all reasonable responses.

2. _____

3. _____

New Vocabulary

Use your text to define each term.

| oxidation-reduction reaction | a reaction in which electrons are transferred from one atom to another |

redox reaction — a simpler term for an oxidation-reduction reaction

oxidation — the loss of electrons from atoms of a substance

reduction — the gain of electrons by atoms of a substance

oxidizing agent — the substance that oxidizes another substance by accepting its electrons

reducing agent — the substance that reduces another substance by losing electrons

Electron Transfer and Redox Reactions

Use with pages 680–682.

Describe *redox reactions by completing the statement below. Use Figure 19.1 in your text as reference.*

A redox reaction consists of two complimentary processes.

Oxidation results in a __loss of electrons__ and an increased

__oxidation number__. Reduction results in a __gain of electrons__ and a

__decreased__ oxidation number.

Section 19.1 Oxidation and Reduction (continued)

Main Idea ———— **Details** ————————————

Oxidizing and Reducing Agents

Use with page 683.

Compare and contrast *an oxidizing agent and a reducing agent.*

An oxidizing agent and a reducing agent both are involved in redox reactions. Both involve a change in the number of electrons of another substance. An oxidizing agent oxidizes another substance by accepting its electrons, while a reducing agent supplies electrons to the substance getting reduced.

Identify Oxidation–Reduction Reactions

Use with Example Problem 19.1, page 685.

Summarize *Fill in the blanks to help you take notes while you read Example Problem 19.1.*

Problem

Write the equation for the redox reaction:

$2Al + 2Fe^{3+} + 3O^{2-} \longrightarrow 2Al^{3+} + 2Fe + 3O^{2-}$

Identify what is __oxidized__ and what is __reduced__ in the redox reaction of aluminum and iron. Identify the __oxidizing agent__ and the __reducing agent__.

1. **Analyze the Problem**

   Known: the ions in the reaction

   Unknown: the electron transfers that take place

2. **Solve for the Unknown**

   Al becomes Al^{3+} and __loses three__ electrons.

   Fe^{3+} becomes Fe and gains __three__ electrons.

3. **Evaluate the Answer**

   Aluminum __lost__ electrons and is __oxidized__.

   It is the __reducing__ agent. Iron __gained__ electrons and is __reduced__. It is the __oxidizing__ agent.

Section 19.1 Oxidation and Reduction (continued)

(Main Idea)——————(Details)————————————————

Determining Oxidation Numbers

Use with page 686.

Describe *the rules for determining oxidation numbers by completing these statements.*

1. The oxidation number of an uncombined atom is ____zero____.

2. The oxidation number of a monatomic ion is equal to ___**the charge of the ion**___.

3. The oxidation number of the more electronegative atom in a molecule or a complex ion is the same as **the charge it would have if it were an ion**.

4. The oxidation number of fluorine, the most electronegative element, when it is bonded to another element is _−1_.

5. The oxidation number of oxygen in compounds is _−2_, except in peroxides where it is _−1_. The oxidation number of oxygen when it bonds to fluorine is ___**positive**___.

6. The oxidation number of hydrogen in most of its compounds is _+1_.

7. The oxidation numbers of the metal atom in the compounds formed by the metals of groups 1 and 2 and aluminum in group 13 are **+1, +2, and +3**, respectively. These oxidation numbers are equal to ___**the number of the valence electrons**___.

8. The sum of the oxidation numbers in a neutral compound is ___**zero**___.

9. The sum of the oxidation numbers of the atoms in a polyatomic ion is equal to ___**the charge of the ion**___.

Oxidation Numbers in Redox Reactions

Use with page 688.

Describe *the redox reaction for the equation listed below. Use the example on page 688 of your text to complete the table, then label the oxidation numbers of the elements in the equation and indicate the change in each.*

$2Al + Fe_2O_3 \rightarrow 2Fe + Al_2O_3$

Element	Oxidation Number	Rule
Al	0	1
Fe in Fe_2O_3	+3	8
O in Fe_2O_3	−2	5
Fe	0	1
Al in Al_2O_3	+3	8
O in Al_2O_3	−2	5

Change: +3 oxidation

Change: −3 reduction

$$\begin{array}{ccc} 0 & +3\ -2 & \\ 2Al + Fe_2O_3 & \longrightarrow & 2Fe + Al_2O_3 \\ & & 0\quad +3\ -2 \end{array}$$

Change: no change in oxidation number

Redox Reactions
Section 19.2 Balancing Redox Equations

Main Idea ———— **Details** ————————————————

Scan *Section 2 of your text, using the checklist below as a guide.*

- Read all section titles.
- Read all boldfaced words.
- Read all formulas.
- Look at all figures and read the captions.
- Think about what you already know about redox reactions.

Write *three facts you discovered about balancing redox reactions.*

1. Accept all reasonable responses._____

2. _____

3. _____

New Vocabulary *Use your text to define this term.*

oxidation-number method

a technique for balancing redox reactions, based on the principle that

the total increase in oxidation numbers (oxidation) must equal the total

decrease in oxidation numbers (reduction) of atoms involved

species

any kind of chemical unit involved in a process

half-reaction

one of the two parts of a redox reaction—the oxidation half

or the reduction half

The Oxidation-Number Method

Use with page 689.

Sequence *the steps for balancing redox reactions by the oxidation-number method.*

__2__ Identify the atoms that are oxidized and the atoms that are reduced.

__1__ Assign oxidation numbers to all atoms in the equation.

__4__ Make the change in oxidation numbers equal in magnitude by adjusting coefficients in the equation.

__5__ If necessary, use the conventional method to balance the remainder of the equation.

__3__ Determine the change in oxidation number for the atoms that are oxidized and for the atoms that are reduced.

Section 19.2 Balancing Redox Equations (continued)

Main Idea ——— **Details** ————————————————————————

The Oxidation-Number Method

Use with Example Problem 19.3, page 690.

Summarize *Fill in the blanks to help you take notes while you read Example Problem 19.3.*

Problem ─·─

Balance the __redox__ equation for the __reaction__ that produces __copper nitrate__.

$Cu + HNO_3 \rightarrow Cu(NO_3)_2 + NO_2 + H_2O$

1. Analyze the Problem

Known:

The formulas for the reactants and __products__ ; the rules for determining __oxidation number__ ; and the fact that the increase in the oxidation number of the __oxidized atoms__ must equal the __decrease in oxidation number__ of the reduced atoms.

Unknown: __the coefficients needed to balance the equation__

2. Solve for the Unknown

Step 1 Assign oxidation numbers to all the atoms in the equation.

0   +1 +5 −2   +2 +5 −2   +4 −2   +1 −2

$Cu + H\ N\ O_3 \rightarrow Cu(N\ O_3)_2 + N\ O_2 + H_2\ O$

Step 2 Identify which atoms are oxidized (using black arrows) and which are reduced (using red arrows).

0   +1 +5 −2   +2 +5 −2   +4 −2   +1 −2

$Cu + H\ N\ O_3 \rightarrow Cu\ (NO_3)_2 + N\ O_2 + H_2\ O$

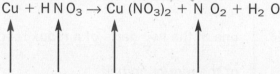

Step 3 Determine the change in oxidation number for the atoms that are oxidized and for the atoms that are reduced. Complete the following tables.

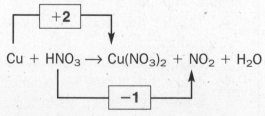

$Cu + HNO_3 \rightarrow Cu(NO_3)_2 + NO_2 + H_2O$

Step 4 To make the net changes in oxidation number have the same magnitude, HNO_3 on the left and NO_2 on the right must be multiplied by __2__ .

Section 19.2 Balancing Redox Equations (continued)

◁Main Idea▷ ——— **◁Details▷** ————————————————

Step 5 Increase the coefficient of HNO_3 from 2 to __4__ to balance the nitrogen atoms in the products. Add a coefficient of __2__ to H_2O to balance the number of hydrogen atoms on the left.

3. Evaluate the Answer

The number of atoms of each element is __equal__ on both sides of the equation. No subscripts have been __changed__.

Balancing Net Ionic Redox Equations

Use with page 691.

Describe *how the form of the balanced equation for the oxidation of copper by nitric acid, below:*

$$Cu(s) + 4HNO_3(aq) \rightarrow Cu(NO_3)_2(aq) + 2NO_2(g) + 2H_2O(l)$$

is changed when rewritten as:

$$Cu(s) + 4H^+(aq) + 4NO_3^-(aq) \rightarrow Cu^{2+}(aq) + 2NO_3^-(aq) + 2NO_2(g) + 2H_2O(l)$$

The second equation is written in ionic form because the aqueous

solution (HNO_3) will be ionized and copper(II) nitrate ($Cu(NO_3)_2$) will

be dissociated into ions.

Balance a Net Ionic Redox Equation

Use with Example Problem 19.4, page 692.

Solve *Read Example Problem 19.4 in your text.*

You Try It

• Problem

Balance the net ionic redox equation for the reaction between the perchlorate ion and the iodide ion in acid solution.

$$ClO_3^-\ (aq) + I^-(aq) \rightarrow Cl^-\ (aq) + I_2(s) \text{ (in acid solution)}$$

1. Analyze the Problem

Known: **the formulas for the reactants and products and**

the rules for determining oxidation number

Unknown: **the coefficients needed to balance the equation**

Section 19.2 Balancing Redox Equations (continued)

Main Idea ——— **Details** ————————————————

2. Solve for the Unknown

Step 1 Assign oxidation numbers to all the atoms in the equation.

$\overset{+5\ -2}{ClO_3^-}$ (aq) + $\overset{-1}{I^-}$(aq) → $\overset{-1}{Cl^-}$(aq) + $\overset{0}{I_2}$(s) (in acid solution)

Step 2 Identify which atoms are oxidized (using black arrows) and which are reduced (using red arrows).

$\overset{+5\ -2}{ClO_3^-}$ (aq) + $\overset{-1}{I^-}$(aq) → $\overset{-1}{Cl^-}$(aq) + $\overset{0}{I_2}$(s) (in acid solution)

Step 3 Determine the change in oxidation number for the atoms that are oxidized and for the atoms that are reduced. Complete the following tables.

$$\boxed{+1}$$

ClO_3^- (aq) + I^-(aq) → Cl^-(aq) + I_2(s) (in acid solution)

$$\boxed{-6}$$

Step 4 To make the net changes in oxidation number have the same magnitude, place the appropriate coefficients in front of the formulas in the equation.

$$\boxed{6(+1) = +6}$$

ClO_3^-(aq) + $6I^-$(aq) → Cl^-(aq) + $3I_2$(s) (in acid solution)

$$\boxed{-6}$$

Step 5 Write an equation that adds enough hydrogen ions and water molecules to balance the oxygen atoms on both sides.

ClO_3^- (aq) + $6I^-$(aq) + $6H^+$(aq) → Cl^-(aq) + $3I_2$(s) + $3H_2O$(l)

3. Evaluate the Answer

The number of atoms of each element is **equal** on both sides of the equation. The net charge on the right **equals** the net charge on the left. No subscripts have been **changed**.

Section 19.2 Balancing Redox Equations (continued)

| Main Idea | Details |

Balancing Redox Equations Using Half-Reactions

Use with pages 693–694.

Identify *the number of species in each reaction. Then, show the oxidation half-reaction and the reduction half-reaction for each equation.*

Reaction	No. of Species	Half-Reaction	
		Oxidation	Reduction
$4Fe + 3O_2 \rightarrow 2Fe_2O_3$	3	$Fe \rightarrow Fe^{3+} + 3e^-$	$O_2 + 4e^- \, 2O^{2-}$
$4Fe + 3Cl_2 \rightarrow 2Fe_2Cl_3$	3	$Fe \rightarrow Fe^{3+} + 3e^-$	$Cl_2 + 2e^- \, 2Cl^-$

Sequence *the steps for balancing by half-reactions.*

__4__ Adjust the coefficients so that the number of electrons lost in oxidation equals the number of electrons gained in reduction.

__1__ Write the net ionic equation for the reaction, omitting spectator ions.

__5__ Add the balanced half-reactions and return spectator ions.

__2__ Write the oxidation and reduction half-reactions for the net ionic equation.

__3__ Balance the atoms and charges in each half-reaction.

Section 19.2 Balancing Redox Reactions (continued)

Main Idea

Balance a Redox Equation by Using Half-Reactions

Use with Example Problem 19.5, page 695.

Details

Summarize *Fill in the blanks to help you take notes while you read Example Problem 19.5.*

• Problem

Balance the redox equation for the <u>**reaction**</u> of permanganate and sulfur dioxide when sulfur dioxide <u>**gas**</u> is bubbled into an <u>**acidic**</u> solution of <u>**potassium permanganate**</u>.

$KMnO_4(aq) + SO_2(g) \rightarrow MnSO_4(aq) + K_2SO_4(aq)$

1. **Analyze the problem**

   Known: <u>the skeleton equation for the reaction of permanganate and sulfur dioxide; reaction takes place in an acid solution</u>

   Unknown: <u>the complete balanced equation for the reaction of permanganate and sulfur dioxide</u>

2. **Solve for the Unknown**

   Step 1: Write the net ionic equation for the reaction:

   $MnO_4^- + SO_2 \rightarrow Mn^{2+} + SO_4^{2-}$

   Step 2: Using rule number 5, the oxidation number for Mn in MnO_4^- is <u>+7</u>. Using rule number 2, the oxidation number for Mn^{2+} is <u>+2</u>. The reduction half-reaction is <u>$MnO_4^- + 5e^- \rightarrow Mn^{2+}$</u>.

   Step 3(a): Balance the atoms and charges in the half-reaction.

   <u>$MnO_4^- + 5e^- \rightarrow Mn^{2+} + 4H_2O$</u>.

Section 19.2 Balancing Redox Reactions (continued)

Main Idea ———— **Details** ————————————————————————

Step 3(b): The __H⁺__ ions are readily available and can be used to balance the charge in half-reactions in acid solutions. The number of H+ ions added to the right side of the oxidation half-reaction is __4__. The number of H+ ions added to the left side of the reduction half-reaction is __8__.

Write the oxidation half-reaction: $SO_2 + 2H_2O \rightarrow SO_4^{2-} + 2e^- + 4H^+$.

Write the reduction half-reaction: $MnO_4^- + 5e^- + 8H^+ \rightarrow Mn^{2+} + 4H_2O$.

Step 4: The number of electrons lost in oxidation is __2__. The number of electrons gained in reduction is __5__. The least common multiple of these numbers is __10__. To balance the half-reactions, the atoms in the oxidation half-reaction must be multiplied by __5__ and the atoms in the reduction half-reaction must be multiplied by __2__. The oxidation half-reaction is now

$5SO_2 + 10H_2O \rightarrow 5SO_4^{2-} + 20H^+ + 10e^-$.

The reduction half-reaction is now

$2MnO_4^- + 16H^+ + 10e^- \rightarrow 2Mn^{2+} + 8H_2O$.

Step 5 After adding the balanced half-reactions, write the redox reaction equation:

$5SO_2 + 10H_2O + 2MnO_4^- + 16H^+ + 10e^- \rightarrow 5SO_4^{2-} + 20H^+ + 10e^- + 2Mn^{2+} + 8 H_2O$.

Cancel or reduce like terms on both sides of the equation, then write the simplified equation:

$5SO_2 + 2H_2O + 2MnO_4^- \rightarrow 5SO_4^{2-} + 4H^+ + 2Mn^{2+}$.

Return spectator ions **(K+)** and restore the state descriptions.

$5SO_2(g) + 2H_2O(l) + 2KMnO_4(aq) \rightarrow K_2SO_4(aq) + 2H_2SO_4(aq) + 2MnSO_4(aq)$.

3. **Evaluate the Answer**

The number of __atoms__ for each element is __equal__ on both sides of the equation and none of the subscripts have been changed.

Redox Reactions Chapter Wrap-Up

After reading this chapter, summarize the processes that occur in a redox reaction.

Accept all reasonable responses. Sample answer: A redox reaction

involves two processes, oxidation and reduction. Oxidation occurs when

the atoms of a substance lose electrons. Reduction occurs when the

atoms of a substance gain electrons. Oxidation cannot occur if reduction

does not occur, and oxidation must occur for reduction to occur.

Review

Use this checklist to help you study.

☐ Study your Science Notebook for this chapter.

☐ Study the definitions of vocabulary words.

☐ Review daily homework assignments.

☐ Reread the chapter and review the tables, graphs, and illustrations.

☐ Review the Section Assessment questions at the end of each section.

☐ Look over the Study Guide at the end of the chapter.

REAL-WORLD CONNECTION

Photosynthesis is an example of a series of naturally occurring redox reactions. In this context, discuss the importance of redox reactions to life on Earth.

Accept all reasonable responses. Sample answer: All forms of life on Earth depend on photosyn-

thesis for their existence. Because photosynthesis involves redox reactions, without them, life on

Earth could not exist. Therefore, redox reactions are essential to maintaining life on Earth.

Electrochemistry

Before You Read

Review Vocabulary *Define the following terms.*

energy | the capacity to do work or produce heat

chemical potential energy | the energy stored in a substance because of its composition

spontaneous process | a physical or chemical change that occurs without outside intervention

and may require energy to be supplied to begin the process

oxidation | the loss of electrons from the atoms of a substance

reduction | the gain of electrons by the atoms of a substance

half-reaction | one of two parts of a redox reaction—the oxidation half, which

shows the number of electrons lost when a species is oxidized, or

the reduction half, which shows the number of electrons gained

when a species is reduced

Chapter 9 **Identify** *three types of reactions.* Accept all reasonable responses. Possible answers:

1. synthesis

2. combustion

3. decomposition

Organize *the following elements from least active to most active. Refer to the activity series in Figure 9.13.*

aluminum, copper, calcium, gold, rubidium, iron, lead, potassium

gold, copper, lead, iron, aluminum, calcium, potassium, rubidium

Electrochemistry
Section 20.1 Voltaic Cells

⟨**Main Idea**⟩ ————— ⟨**Details**⟩ ————————————————

Skim *Section 1 of your text. Focus on the headings, subheadings, boldfaced words, and the main ideas. Summarize three main ideas of this section.*

1. Accept all reasonable answers._____

2. _____

3. _____

⟨**New Vocabulary**⟩ *Use your text to define each term.*

salt bridge — a pathway constructed to allow the passage of ions from one side to another

electrochemical cell — an apparatus that uses a redox reaction to produce electrical energy

or uses electrical energy to cause a chemical reaction

voltaic cell — a type of electrochemical cell that converts chemical energy to

electrical energy by a spontaneous redox reaction

half-cell — each of the two parts of an electrochemical cell in which the

separate oxidation and reduction reactions take place

anode — the electrode where oxidation take place

cathode — the electrode where reduction takes place

reduction potential — the tendency of a substance to gain electrons

standard hydrogen electrode — the standard electrode against which the reduction potential of

all electrodes can be measured

⟨**Academic Vocabulary**⟩ *Define the following term.*

correspond — to be in agreement or to match

Section 20.1 Voltaic Cells (continued)

Main Idea	Details

Redox in Electrochemistry

Use with pages 708–709.

Explain *the branch of chemistry called electrochemistry.*

Electrochemistry is the study of the process by which chemical

energy is converted to electrical energy and vice versa.

Write *the half-reactions of copper and zinc.*

$Cu^{2+} + 2e^- \rightarrow Cu$ (reduction half-reaction: electrons **gained**)

$Zn \rightarrow Zn^{2+} + 2e^-$ (oxidation half-reaction: electrons **lost**)

Explain *how an electrochemical cell uses a redox reaction.*

An electrochemical cell uses a redox reaction to produce electrical

energy or uses electrical energy to cause a chemical reaction.

Chemistry of Voltaic Cells

Use with page 710.

Complete *each of the following statements.*

1. The electrode where oxidation takes place is called the **anode** .

2. The electrode where reduction takes place is called the **cathode** .

3. An object's potential energy is **due to position or composition** .

4. In electrochemistry, **electrical potential energy** is a measure of

the amount of **current** that can be generated from a **voltaic cell**

to do work.

Sequence *the steps of the electrochemical process that occur in a zinc-copper voltaic cell. The first one has been done for you.*

_4_ To complete the circuit, both positive and negative ions move through the salt bridge. The two half-reactions can be summed to show the overall cell reaction.

_2_ The electrons flow from the zinc strip and pass through the external circuit to the copper strip.

_1_ Electrons are produced in the oxidation half-cell according to this half-reaction: $Zn(s) \rightarrow Zn^{2+}(aq) + 2e^-$.

_3_ Electrons enter the reduction half-cell where the following half-reaction occurs: $Cu^{2+}(aq) + 2e^- \rightarrow Cu(s)$.

Section 20.1 Voltaic Cells (continued)

Main Idea	Details

Calculating Electrochemical Cell Potential

Use with pages 711–712.

Describe *reduction potential in relation to an electrode.*

Reduction potential of an electrode is the tendency of a substance

to gain electrons. It cannot be measured directly because the reduction

half-reaction must be coupled with an oxidation half-reaction.

Analyze *Table 20.1. Some of the E^0 (V)s are positive, some are negative. Explain the difference.*

All of the half-reactions are written as reductions. The half-reaction that

is more positive will proceed as a reduction and the half-reaction that is

more negative will proceed as an oxidation.

Write *the abbreviated E^0 and half-reaction for each of the following:*

Element	Half-Reaction	E^0 (V)
Li	$Li^+ + e^- \rightarrow Li$	−3.0401
Au	$Au^+ + e^- \rightarrow Au$	1.692
PbSO$_4$	$PbSO_4 + 2e^- \rightarrow Pb + SO_4^{2-}$	−0.3588
Na	$Na^+ + e^- \rightarrow Na$	−2.71

Calculate a Cell Potential

Use with Example Problem 20.1, page 715.

Summarize *Fill the blanks to help you take notes while you read Example Problem 20.1.*

Problem – •

Calculate the overall cell reaction and the standard potential for the half-cells of a voltaic cell.

$$I_2(s) + 2e^- \rightarrow 2I^-(aq)$$

$$Fe^{2+}(aq) + 2e^- \rightarrow Fe(s)$$

1. Analyze the Problem.

List the known and the unknown.

Known: Standard reduction potentials for the half-cells

$$E^0_{cell} = E^0_{reduction} - E^0_{oxidation}$$

Unknown: $E^0_{cell} = ?$, overall cell reaction = ?, cell notation = ?

Section 20.1 Voltaic Cells (continued)

(Main Idea)	(Details)

2. Solve for the unknown.

Find the standard reduction potentials for half-reactions.

$E^0_{I_2|I^-}$ = __+0.536 V__

$E^0_{Fe^{2+}|Fe}$ = __−0.447 V__

Rewrite the half−reactions in the correct direction.

reduction half−cell reaction: __$I_2(s) + 2e^- \rightarrow 2I^-(aq)$__

oxidation half−cell reaction: __$Fe(s) \rightarrow Fe^{2+}(aq) + 2e^-$__

overall cell reaction: __oxidized__ $I_2(s) + Fe(s) \rightarrow Fe^{2+}(aq) + 2I^-(aq)$

Balance the reaction if necessary:

__equation is balanced__

Calculate cell standard potential:

$E^U_{cell} = E^0_{reduction} - E^0_{oxidation}$

E^0_{cell} = +0.536 V − __(−0.447 V)__

E^0_{cell} = + __0.983 V__

Write the reaction using cell notation:

__$Fe \mid Fe^{2+} \parallel I_2 \mid I^-$__

3. Evaluate the answer.

The answer seems reasonable given the __reduction potentials__

of the __half-cells__ that comprise it.

Using Standard Reduction Potentials

Use with page 716.

Write *the steps for the process of predicting whether any proposed redox reaction will occur spontaneously.*

1. __Write the process in the form of half-reactions.__

2. __Look up the reduction potential of each.__

3. __Use the values to calculate the potential of a voltaic cell operating with these two half-cell reactions.__

4. __If the calculated potential is positive, the reaction is spontaneous.__

5. __If the calculated potential is negative, the reaction is not spontaneous.__

Electrochemistry

Section 20.2 Batteries

Skim *Section 2 of your text. Write three questions that come to mind after reading the headings and the illustration captions.* **Accept all reasonable responses.**

1. _____

2. _____

3. _____

New Vocabulary

Use your text to define each term.

battery	one or more electrochemical cells in a single package that generates electrical current
dry cell	an electrochemical cell in which the electrolyte is a moist paste
primary battery	battery that produces electric energy by means of redox reactions that are not easily reversed
secondary battery	battery that is rechargeable due to a reversible redox reaction
fuel cell	a voltaic cell in which the oxidation of a fuel is used to produce electric energy
corrosion	the loss of metal resulting from an oxidation-reduction reaction of the metal with substances in the environment
galvanization	a process in which iron is coated with a layer of zinc by either dipping the iron object into molten zinc or by electroplating the zinc onto it

Section 20.2 Batteries (continued)

Main Idea — **Details** _____

Dry Cells

Use with pages 718–720.

Write *the oxidation half-reaction for the dry cell of the most commonly used voltaic cell.*

$Zn(s) \rightarrow Zn^{2+}(aq) + 2e^-$

List *the paste and cathode type for each of the following batteries. So-called dry cell batteries contain different moist pastes in which the cathode half-reaction takes place.*

Zinc-carbon battery

Paste $ZnCl_2$, MnO_2, NH_4Cl (electrolyte)

Cathode type   Carbon rod

Alkaline battery

Paste   Zn-KOH

Cathode type MnO_2

Mercury battery

Paste $Zn(OH)_2$ and HgO

Cathode type   Steel

Compare and contrast *primary and secondary batteries.*

Primary batteries are throwaway types. These cells deliver current

until the reactants are gone. In secondary batteries, the reaction

runs as with a primary battery except the redox reaction is

reversible, therefore, the battery can be recharged.

Explain *how NiCad batteries, often found in cordless tools and phones, are recharged.*

Cordless tools and phones sit on a base that is plugged into an

electrical outlet. The electrical outlet supplies the power to drive the

nonspontaneous recharge reaction.

Section 20.2 Batteries (continued)

Main Idea	Details

Lead-Acid Storage Battery

Use with pages 720–721.

Explain *how the following overall reaction of lead-acid batteries is different from traditional redox reactions.*

$$Pb(s) + PbO_2(s) + 4H^+(aq) + 2SO_4^{2-}(aq) \rightarrow 2PbSO_4(s) + 2H_2O(l)$$

It is different from other reactions because PbSO₄ is the reaction product in
both oxidation and reduction. Also, Pb, PbO₂, and PbSO₄ are solid, so they
stay in place where they are formed. Thus, whether the battery is discharg-
ing or charging, the reactants are available where they are needed.

Lithium Batteries

Use with pages 721–722.

List *two reasons that scientists and engineers have focused a lot of attention on the element lithium to make batteries.*

1. less mass—lithium is the lightest known metal

2. lithium has the lowest standard reduction potential of the metallic elements

Describe *two applications of lightweight lithium batteries.*

Accept all reasonable responses. Possible answers: watches,

computers, cameras

Fuel Cells

Use with pages 722–723.

Explain *the makeup of a fuel cell by completing the following paragraph and accompanying reactions.*

In a fuel cell, each electrode is a hollow chamber of porous carbon walls

that allows contact between the inner chamber and the electrolyte

surrounding it . The walls of the chamber also contain catalysts,

such as powdered platinum or palladium, which speed up the reactions.

oxidation half-reaction: $2H_2(g) + 4OH^-(aq) \rightarrow 4H_2O(l) + 4e^-$

reduction half-reaction: $O_2(g) + 2H_2O(l) + 4e^- \rightarrow 4OH^-(aq)$

overall cell reaction: $2H_2(g) + O_2(g) \rightarrow 2H_2O(l)$

The overall cell reaction is the same as the equation for the burning

of hydrogen in oxygen .

List *three reasons why PEMs are used instead of a liquid electrode.*

1. non-corrosive

2. safer

3. lighter in weight

Section 20.2 Batteries (continued)

Main Idea	Details

Corrosion

Use with pages 724–727.

Compare *rusting of metal to redox reactions in voltaic cells.*

They are both spontaneous redox reactions. Rusting is a spontaneous

redox reaction between iron and oxygen (though a bit more complex)

while the redox reactions in a voltaic cell are between other elements.

Draw *and label the parts of the corrosion reaction in Figure 20.15. Be sure to identify the anode and cathode.*

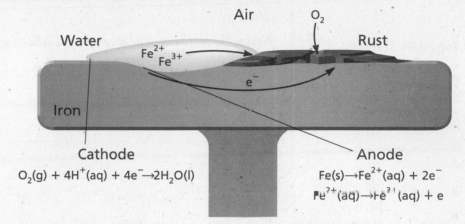

Air

O_2

Water

Fe^{2+}
Fe^{3+}

Rust

e^-

Iron

Cathode
$O_2(g) + 4H^+(aq) + 4e^- \rightarrow 2H_2O(l)$

Anode
$Fe(s) \rightarrow Fe^{2+}(aq) + 2e^-$
$Fe^{2+}(aq) \rightarrow Fe^{3+}(aq) + e$

Explain *why rusting is a slow process. List a way that it might be sped up in certain areas.*

Water droplets have few ions and are not good electrolytes. If water

contains abundant ions, as in seawater or in regions where roads are

salted in winter, corrosion occurs much faster because the solutions

are excellent electrolytes.

Explain *the two ways galvanizing helps prevent corrosion.*

1. The zinc coating seals the iron from air and water by forming a

barrier of zinc oxide that repels water and oxygen. As long as the

zinc layer is intact, water and oxygen cannot reach the iron's surface.

2. If the zinc-coating barrier is broken, the zinc protects iron from

rapid corrosion by becoming the anode of the voltaic cell set up

when water and oxygen contact iron and zinc at the same time.

Electrochemistry
Section 20.3 Electrolysis

Main Idea ———— **Details** ——————————————————

Scan *Section 3 of your text. Use the checklist below as a guide.*

• Read all section titles.

• Read all boldfaced words.

• Read all formulas.

• Look at all figures and read the captions.

• Think about what you already know about electrolysis.

Write *three facts you discovered about electrolysis as you scanned the section.*

1. Accept all reasonable responses. _____

2. _____

3. _____

New Vocabulary   *Use your text to define each term.*

electrolysis   the use of electrical energy to bring about a chemical reaction

electrolytic cell   an electrochemical cell in which electrolysis occurs

Section 20.3 Electrolysis (continued)

Main Idea	Details

Reversing Redox Reactions

Use with page 728.

Describe *how it is possible to reverse a spontaneous redox reaction in an electrochemical cell.*

A current is passed through the cell in the opposite direction. The

energy of the current reverses the cell redox reaction and regenerates

the original substances.

Applications of Electrolysis

Use with pages 729–732.

Compare *the reactions involved in sodium chloride to those in the electrolysis of brine.*

Electrolysis can decompose molten sodium chloride into sodium

metal and chlorine gas, using a Down's cell. The decomposition of

brine, an aqueous solution of sodium chloride, produces hydrogen

gas, chlorine gas, and sodium hydroxide.

Explain *the importance of electrolysis in the purification of metals.*

Impure molten copper is cast into large, thick plates, which are used

as an anode in an electrolytic cell containing copper(II) sulfate. The

cathode is a thin sheet of pure copper. As current is passed through

the cell, copper atoms in the impure anode are oxidized to copper(II)

ions, which migrate through the solution to the cathode where they

are reduced to pure Cu atoms. These atoms become part of the

cathode. The impurities fall to the bottom of the cell.

Electrochemistry Chapter Wrap-Up

After reading this chapter, list three important facts you have learned about electrochemistry. **Accept all reasonable responses. Possible answers:**

1. electrical energy can be used to create a chemical reaction and chemicals can be used to create electrical energy

2. redox reactions are divided into two half-reactions where oxidation and reduction reactions take place

3. electrolysis is useful in purifying metals

Review

Use this checklist to help you study.

☐ Study your Science Notebook for this chapter.

☐ Study the definitions of vocabulary words.

☐ Review daily homework assignments.

☐ Reread the chapter and review the tables, graphs, and illustrations.

☐ Review the Section Assessment questions at the end of each section.

☐ Look over the Study Guide at the end of the chapter.

REAL-WORLD CONNECTION

Describe how electrochemistry is involved in producing energy in batteries.

All electrical energies produced by batteries are based upon half-cell reactions. In addition, the chemical properties of the elements used in batteries play a role in determining both the amount of energy generated by the battery and the battery's useful life.

Hydrocarbons

Before You Read

Review Vocabulary	**Define** *each term.*	
covalent bond	a bond that occurs when distinct atoms share valence electrons in order to become stable	
Lewis structure	a means of using electron dot diagrams to show how electrons are arranged in molecules	

Chapter 8   **Draw** *the Lewis structure for NH₃.*

$$H - \ddot{N} - H$$
$$|$$
$$H$$

Chapter 12   **Compare and contrast** *melting and boiling.*

Melting and boiling both involve phase changes. In melting, a solid becomes a liquid. In boiling, a liquid becomes a gas.

Hydrocarbons

Section 21.1 Introduction to Hydrocarbons

Main Idea ——————   **Details** ——————————————————

Scan *Section 1 of your text. Use the checklist below as a guide.*

• Read all section titles.

• Read all boldfaced words.

• Look at all pictures and read the captions

• Think about what you already know about this subject.

Write *three facts you discovered about hydrocarbons.*
Accept all reasonable responses. Possible answers:

1. Hydrocarbons contain only the elements hydrogen and carbon.

2. Carbon atoms bond to each other with single, double, and triple

covalent bonds.

3. Many hydrocarbons are obtained from petroleum, a fossil fuel.

New Vocabulary   *Use your text to define each term.*

organic compound   carbon-containing compound, with the exceptions of carbon oxides,

carbides, and carbonates

hydrocarbon   compounds containing only the elements carbon and hydrogen—

the simplest organic compounds

saturated hydrocarbon   a hydrocarbon having only single bonds

unsaturated hydrocarbon   a hydrocarbon that has at least one double or triple bond between

carbon atoms

fractional distillation   separation of petroleum into simpler components

cracking   process by which heavier fractions of petroleum are broken into

smaller molecules

Section 21.1 Introduction to Hydrocarbons (continued)

⟨**Main Idea**⟩———— ⟨**Details**⟩——————————————————————

Organic Compounds

Use with pages 744–745.

Explain *the evolution of the contemporary understanding of the term organic compound.*

> In the early nineteenth century, chemists referred to the variety of carbon compounds produced by living things as **organic compounds**.

↓

> Using Dalton's atomic model, chemists were able to synthesize substances, but not carbon compounds. This failure was due to their belief in vitalism, which meant that they needed a mysterious "vital force" to assemble carbon compounds. Wohler's experiment, in which he synthesized urea, started a chain of similar experiments that discredited vitalism.

↓

> Today the term **organic compound** is applied to all carbon-containing compounds with the primary exceptions of carbon oxides, carbides, and carbonates, which are considered inorganic.

Explain *why many compounds contain carbon by completing the following statements.*

Carbon's __electron configuration__ allows it to make four covalent bonds.

In organic compounds, carbon atoms bond to __hydrogen atoms__ or

other elements near carbon on the periodic table. Carbon atoms also

bond to __other carbon atoms__ and can form long __chains__ .

Hydrocarbons

Use with pages 745–746.

Label *the web below with the correct name for each model of methane.*

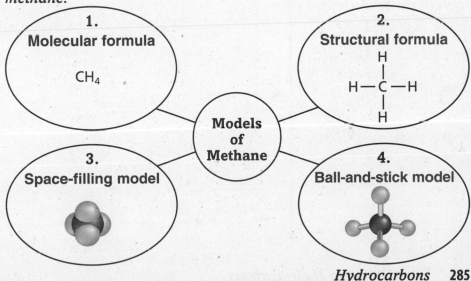

1. Molecular formula

CH_4

2. Structural formula

$$H-\overset{\displaystyle H}{\underset{\displaystyle H}{C}}-H$$

Models of Methane

3. Space-filling model

4. Ball-and-stick model

Section 21.1 Introduction to Hydrocarbons (continued)

Main Idea ———

Details ——————————————————

Multiple Carbon-Carbon Bonds

Use with page 746.

Organize *the outline below.*

I. Ways that carbon atoms bond to each other

    A. single covalent bonds

        1. share **one pair of electrons**

        2. also called **a saturated hydrocarbon**

    B. double covalent bonds

        1. share **two pairs of electrons**

        2. also called **an unsaturated hydrocarbon**

    C. triple covalent bonds

        1. share **three pairs of electrons**

        2. also called **an unsaturated hydrocarbon**

Draw *models of each carbon-carbon bond and label them appropriately. Use the illustrations on page 710 of your text as a guide.*

Single Covalent Bond	Double Covalent Bond	Triple Covalent Bond
$-\overset{\mid}{\underset{\mid}{C}}-\overset{\mid}{\underset{\mid}{C}}-$	$\overset{\diagdown}{\diagup}C=C\overset{\diagup}{\diagdown}$	$-C\equiv C-$

Section 21.1 Introduction to Hydrocarbons (continued)

Main Idea	Details

Refining Hydrocarbons

Use with pages 747–748.

Identify *natural sources of hydrocarbons by completing the following statements.*

The main natural source of hydrocarbons is <u>petroleum</u>, a complex mixture containing more than a thousand <u>different compounds</u>. Petroleum is more useful to humans when <u>it is separated into simpler components</u>, called <u>fractions</u>. Separation is carried out by <u>boiling the petroleum and collecting the fractions as they condense at different temperatures</u>, a process called fractional distillation.

Sequence *the process of fractional distillation.*

_3_ Vapors travel up through the column.

_1_ Temperature is controlled to remain near 400° at the bottom of the fractionating tower.

_5_ Hydrocarbons with fewer carbon atoms remain in the vapor phase until they reach regions of cooler temperatures farther up the column.

_4_ Hydrocarbons with more carbon atoms condense closer to the bottom or the tower and are drawn off.

_2_ Petroleum boils and gradually moves toward the top.

Match the names of these two processes with their definitions.

1. fractional distillation   2. cracking

___Cracking___ is done to break the larger molecules of petroleum components into smaller molecules.

<u>Fractional distillation</u> separates petroleum into simpler components.

Rating Gasoline

Use with pages 748–749.

Explain *why branched-chain alkanes make better gasolines than straight-chain hydrocarbons.*

Accept all reasonable responses. Possible answer: Most straight-chain hydrocarbons burn unevenly and tend to ignite too early or too late. Early ignition causes knocking. Branched-chain alkanes burn more evenly which helps prevent knocking.

Hydrocarbons
Section 21.2 Alkanes

Main Idea	Details
	Skim *Section 2 of your text. Write three questions that come to mind from reading the headings and the illustration captions.*

1. Accept all reasonable responses._____

2. _____

3. _____

_____

New Vocabulary *Use your text to define each term.*

alkane	hydrocarbons that have only single bonds between atoms
homologous series	a series of compounds that differ from one another by a repeating unit
parent chain	the longest continuous chain of carbon atoms
substituent group	side branch of a parent chain that appears to substitute for a
	hydrogen atom in the straight chain
cyclic hydrocarbon	an organic compound that contains a hydrocarbon ring
cycloalkane	a cyclic hydrocarbon that contains a single bond only

Academic Vocabulary *Define the following terms.*

substitute	a person or thing that takes the place of another

Section 21.2 Alkanes

Main Idea ——   **Details** ———————————————————

Straight-Chain Alkanes

Use with pages 750–751.

Compare and contrast *the models in the table below.*

Type of Model	Description of Model
1. Molecular formula	gives no information about the geometry of the molecule
2. Structural formula	shows the general arrangement of atoms but not the exact geometry
3. Space-filling model	give a more realistic picture of what a molecule would look like if you could see it
4. Ball-and-stick model	demonstrate the geometry of the molecule more clearly

Describe *straight-chain alkanes by completing the following sentences.*

The first four compounds in the straight-chain series of alkanes are __methane, ethane, propane, and butane__. The names of all alkanes end in __–ane__. Because the first four alkanes were named before there was a complete understanding of alkane structures, their names do not have __numerical prefixes__ as do the alkanes with __five or more carbons__ in a chain. Chemists use __condensed structural formulas__ to save space.

Explain *the structural formula of the following hydrocarbons. The first has been done for you.*

1. Methane is formed from one atom of carbon and four atoms of hydrogen.

2. Butane is formed __from four atoms of carbon and ten atoms of hydrogen__.

3. Octane is formed __from eight atoms of carbon and eighteen atoms of hydrogen__.

4. Decane is formed __from ten atoms of carbon and twenty-two atoms of hydrogen__.

Analyze *how the function of a homologous series is evidenced in the condensed structural formula of nonane.*

The relationship between the numbers of carbon and hydrogen atoms in a homologous series can be expressed as C_nH_{2n+2}—. It can be expressed as $(CH_2)_7$, representing seven carbon atoms and fourteen hydrogen atoms.

Section 21.2 Alkanes (continued)

⟨Main Idea⟩	⟨Details⟩

Branched-Chain Alkanes

Use with page 752.

Compare *three characteristics of butane and isobutane.*

The carbon atoms of butane are arranged in a zigzag fashion. The outer carbon

atoms are each bonded to three hydrogen atoms. The two inner carbon atoms

are each bonded to two other carbon atoms and two hydrogen atoms.

The carbon atoms of isobutane are in straight lines in respect to one another.

The three outer carbon atoms are each bonded to the middle carbon atom as

well as three hydrogen atoms. The middle carbon atom is bonded to the three

outer carbon atoms and one hydrogen atom.

Naming Branched-Chain Alkanes

Use with page 753.

Describe *naming branched-chain alkanes.*

A straight-chain and a branched-chain alkane can have the same molecular formula.

PRINCIPLE
Therefore, the name of an organic compound also must describe the molecular structure of the compound accurately.

NAMING PROCESS
Branched-chain alkanes are viewed as consisting of a straight chain of carbon atoms or groups of carbon atoms branching off the straight chain.

NAMING, PART 1
The longest continuous chain of carbon atoms is called the parent chain.

NAMING, PART 2
All side branches are called substituent groups because they appear to substitute for a hydrogen atom in the straight chain.

NAMING, PART 3
Each alkane-based substituent group branching from the parent chain is named for the straight-chain alkane having the same number of carbon atoms as the substituent by replacing the ending –*ane* with the letters –*yl*.

Section 21.2 Alkanes (continued)

Main Idea ———   **Details** ——————————————————————

Cycloalkanes

Use with pages 755–756.

Organize *the concept web below.*

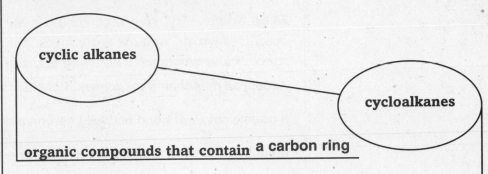

organic compounds that contain **a carbon ring**

the prefix *cyclo-* indicates a **hydrocarbon with a ring structure**

possible to have three, four, five, six, or even more **carbon atoms**

represented by condensed, skeletal, **and line structure**

can have **substituent** groups

Properties of Alkanes

Use with pages 757–758.

Classify *the properties of alkanes into categories.*

General Properties (3)	Physical Properties (4)	Chemical Properties (2)
bonds between either a carbon atom and a hydrogen atom or two carbon atoms	little intermolecular attraction affects melting and boiling points	low reactivity
bonds are not polar	do not form hydrogen bonds	readily undergo combustion in oxygen
alkane molecules are nonpolar	immiscibility with water	
	more soluble in solvents composed of nonpolar molecules	

Hydrocarbons
Section 21.3 Alkenes and Alkynes

Main Idea ———

Details ————————————————————————

Scan *Section 3 of your text. Focus on the headings, subheadings, boldfaced words, and the main ideas. Set the book aside and, in the space below, summarize the main ideas of this section.*

Accept all reasonable responses. Possible answer: Alkenes must have

a double covalent bond between carbon atoms. This differentiates

them from alkynes, which have at least one triple bond. The properties

of alkenes and alkynes are different than those of alkanes. The IUPAC

rules can be used to name the hydrocarbons.

New Vocabulary *Use your text to define each term.*

alkene ___ an unsaturated hydrocarbon that contains one or more double

covalent bonds between carbon atoms in a chain

alkyne ___ an unsaturated hydrocarbon that contains one or more triple bonds

between carbon atoms in a chain

Section 21.3 Alkenes and Alkynes (continued)

Main Idea	Details

Alkenes

Use with pages 759–760.

Identify *five facts about alkenes as discussed in your text.*

1. Because an alkene must have a double bond between carbon atoms, there is no 1-carbon alkene.

2. The simplest alkene has two carbon atoms double-bonded to each other.

3. The remaining four electrons are shared with four hydrogen atoms to give the molecule ethene.

4. Alkenes with only one double bond constitute a homologous series.

5. The general formula for the series is C_nH_{2n}.

Sequence *the factors involved in naming an alkene with four or more carbons in the chain using the web below and number the steps.*

1. Change the *–ane* ending of the corresponding alkane to *–ene*

2. Specify the location of the double bond

Naming Alkenes

3. Number the carbons in the parent chain starting at the end of the chain that will give the first carbon in the double bond the lowest number

4. Use only that number in the name

Naming Branched-Chain Alkenes

Use with Example Problem 21.3, page 761.

Summarize *Use the following to help you take notes as you read Example Problem 21.3 in your text.*

Problem — · — · — · — · — · — · — · — · — · —

Name the following alkene.

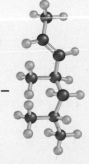

Section 21.3 Alkenes and Alkynes (continued)

Main Idea ———— **Details** ————————————————

1. **Analyze the Problem**

   You are given a branch-chained alkene that contains one double bond and two alkyl groups. Follow the IUPAC rules to name the organic compound.

2. **Solve for the Unknown**

   a. The longest continuous carbon chain that includes the double bond contains **seven** carbons. The **7-carbon** alkane is heptane, but the name is changed to **heptene** because a double bond is present.

   $$CH_3CH \quad CHCHCH_2CHCH_3$$

   b. and c. Number the chain to give the lowest number to the double bond and name each substituent.

   $$\overset{1}{C}H_3\overset{2}{C}H \quad \overset{3}{C}H\overset{4}{C}H\overset{5}{C}H_2\overset{6}{C}H\overset{7}{C}H_3$$

   d. Determine how many of each substituent is present, and assign the correct prefix to represent that number. Then, include the position numbers to get the complete prefix.

   $$\overset{1}{C}H_3\overset{2}{C}H \quad \overset{3}{C}H\overset{4}{C}H\overset{5}{C}H_2\overset{6}{C}H\overset{7}{C}H_3$$
   $$\qquad\qquad\quad | \qquad\quad |$$
   $$\qquad\qquad CH_3 \quad CH_3$$

   e. The names of substituents **do not have to be alphabetized because they are the same**.

   f. Apply the complete prefix to the name of the parent alkene chain. Use commas to separate numbers and hyphens between numbers and words. Write the name **4,6-dimethyl-2-heptene**.

3. **Evaluate the Answer**

   The longest carbon chain includes the **double bond**, and the position of the double bond has the **lowest possible number**. Correct prefixes and alkyl-group names **designate the branches**.

Alkynes

Use with pages 762–764.

Compare and contrast *alkenes and alkynes.*

Both are unsaturated carbons with a high level of reactivity. An alkene must

have a double bond between atoms, while an alkyne must have a triple bond.

Hydrocarbons
Section 21.4 Hydrocarbon Isomers

Main Idea ——— **Details** ———————————————————

Skim *Section 4 of your text. Write two questions that come to mind from reading the headings and the illustration captions.*

1. Accept all reasonable responses._____

2. _____

New Vocabulary *Use your text to define each term.*

isomer two or more compounds that have the same molecular formula but

different molecular structures

structural isomer isomers in which the atoms are bonded in different orders and that have

different chemical and physical properties despite having the same formula

stereoisomer isomers in which all atoms are bonded in the same order but are

arranged differently in space

geometric isomer isomers that result from different arrangements of groups around a double bond

chirality property of compounds that exist in right and left forms

asymmetric carbon a carbon atom that has four different atoms or groups of atoms attached to it

optical isomer isomers that result from different arrangements of four different groups

about the same carbon atom; they have the same physical and chemical

properties except in chemical reactions where chirality is important

optical rotation results when polarized light passes through a solution containing an

optical isomer and the plane of polarization is rotated to the right by

a D-isomer or to the left by an L-isomer

Section 21.4 Hydrocarbon Isomers (continued)

Main Idea	Details

Structural Isomers

Use with page 765.

Organize *the outline below.*

I. <u>Isomers</u>:Two or more compounds that have the same molecular formula but different molecular structures.

  A. Two types of isomers

    1. Structural isomers

      a. <u>The atoms are bonded in different orders</u>

      b. <u>Have different chemical and physical properties despite having the same formula</u>

        i. Examples include <u>pentane, 2-methylbutane, and 2,2-dimethylpropane</u>

Stereoisomers

Use with page 766.

    2. Stereoisomers

      a. <u>All atoms are bonded in the same order but are arranged differently in space</u>

        i. <u>Two carbon atoms with a single bond rotate freely</u>

        ii. <u>Two carbon atoms with a double bond are locked in place</u>

      b. <u>Geometric isomers</u>

        i. Result from different arrangements of groups around a double bond

      1. Possible _____<u>health risks</u>_____ with *trans*-fatty acids.

      2. The <u>*cis*- forms of the same acids</u> seem not to be as harmful.

Chiralty

Use with page 767.

Describe *chirality by completing the flow chart below.*

Chirality occurs whenever	→	a compound contains an asymmetric carbon,	→	which has four different atoms or groups of atoms attached to it.

These isomers are called optical isomers.	←	The molecules are different even though they look very much alike.	←	The four groups can be arranged in two different ways.

Name_____   Date _____

Section 21.4 Hydrocarbon Isomers (continued)

Main Idea	Details

Optical Isomers

Use with pages 768–769.

Identify *the types of isomers shown below. Which pair are optical isomers?*

D-glyceraldehyde and L-glyceraldehyde

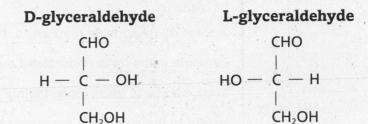

D-glyceraldehyde	L-glyceraldehyde

optical isomer

ethanol	**methoxymethane**

structural isomer

***trans*-1,2-dichloroethene**	***cis*-1,2-dichloroethene**

geometric isomer

COMPARE

Explain what a pair of shoes and crystals of the organic compound tartaric acid have in common.

A right shoe and a left shoe are mirror images of each other as are D-tartaric acid and L-tartaric

acid—*D* meaning *dextro-*, or *to the right,* and *L* meaning *levo-*, or *to the left.* Living organisms

make use of only one chiral form of a substance because only this form fits the active site of an

enzyme, just as a right shoe will only fit the right foot.

Hydrocarbons   **297**

Hydrocarbons
Section 21.5 Aromatic Hydrocarbons

Main Idea ———— **Details** —————————————————————

Skim *Section 5 of your text. Focus on the headings, subheadings, boldfaced words, and the main ideas. Summarize the main ideas of this section.*

Accept all reasonable responses. Possible answer: The model of

benzene helps us to understand aromatic and aliphatic hydrocarbons.

Their source is fossil fuels, mainly petroleum, a complex mixture more

useful to humans when separated by fractional distillation and then

further broken down by the process of cracking.

New Vocabulary *Use your text to define each term.*

aromatic compound | an organic compound that contains benzene rings as part of its structure

aliphatic compound | hydrocarbons such as the alkanes, alkenes, and alkynes

Section 21.5 Aromatic Hydrocarbons (continued)

Main Idea ——   **Details** ———————————————————

Aromatic Compounds

Use with pages 771–772.

Classify *the properties of aromatic and aliphatic compounds.*

	Structural Characteristics	Reactivity
Aromatic Compounds	contain single benzene rings, sometimes two or more benzene rings fused together	less reactive
Aliphatic Compounds	contain single, double, and triple bonds	more reactive

Model *Draw a model of a fused ring system.*

Possible answer: Student may draw something that resembles naphthalene or anthracene.

Explain *how substituted benzene rings are numbered.*

Substituted benzene rings are numbered in a way that gives the

lowest possible numbers for the substituents.

Number *the substituted benzene ring in the structure below, then name the structure.*

2-Ethyl-1,4-dimethylbenzene

Hydrocarbons Chapter Wrap-Up

Now that you have read the chapter, review what you have learned; list the types of models used to represent chemical compounds and name the different categories of hydrocarbons.

Hydrocarbons:

Alkanes

    Straight-chain alkanes

    Branched-chain alkanes

    Cycloalkanes

Alkenes

    Branched-chain alkenes

Alkynes

Isomers

    Structural isomers

    Geometric isomers

Aromatic **compounds**

Models:

Molecular formula

Structural formula

Ball-and-stick model

Space-filling model

Stereoisomers

Optical isomers

Aliphatic **compounds**

Review   *Use this checklist to help you study.*

☐ Study your Science Notebook for this chapter.

☐ Study the definitions of vocabulary words.

☐ Review daily homework assignments.

☐ Reread the chapter and review the tables, graphs, and illustrations.

☐ Review the Section Assessment questions at the end of each section.

☐ Look over the Study Guide at the end of the chapter.

SUMMARIZE Explain how hydrocarbons have contributed to space exploration.

Accept all reasonable responses. Possible answer: The most important contribution has been the

fuel needed for spacecrafts to travel beyond our planet. In addition, materials made from

hydrocarbons are used in the spacecrafts as well as in the astronaut's gear and their equipment.

Substituted Hydrocarbons and Their Reactions

Before You Read

Review Vocabulary   *Define the following terms.*

periodic table	a table that organizes the elements into a grid of rows and columns according to their chemical and physical properties
compound	a combination of two or more different elements that are chemically combined
halogens	highly reactive elements, group 7A in the periodic table
chemical bond	the force that holds two atoms together
catalyst	a substance that increases the rate of a chemical reaction without itself being consumed

Chapter 21   **Compare and contrast** *stereoisomers with structural isomers.* Structural isomers are isomers that have the same chemical formula but are bonded in a different order. They have different chemical and physical properties due to their structure. Stereoisomers are bonded in the same order, but are arranged differently in space. They have different chemical and physical properties due to their arrangement in space.

Substituted Hydrocarbons and Their Reactions

Section 22.1 Alkyl Halides and Aryl Halides

Main Idea ————— **Details** ——————————————————

Skim *Section 1 of your text. Write three questions that come to mind from reading the headings and the illustration captions.*

1. Accept all reasonable responses._____

2. _____

3. _____

New Vocabulary *Use your text to define each term.*

functional group | an atom or group of atoms in an organic molecule that always reacts

in a certain way

halocarbon | any organic compound that contains a halogen substituent

alkyl halide | an organic compound containing a halogen atom covalently bonded

to an aliphatic carbon atom

aryl halide | an organic compound containing a halogen atom bonded to a

benzene ring or other aromatic group

substitution reaction | a reaction in which one atom or group of atoms in a molecule is

replaced by another atom or group of atoms

halogenation | with alkanes, a process in which hydrogen atoms may be replaced

by atoms of halogens, typically chlorine or bromine

Section 22.1 Alkyl Halides and Aryl Halides (continued)

Main Idea ——— **Details** ————————————————————

Functional Groups

Use with pages 786–787.

Describe *how a functional group can be helpful in determining how a molecule reacts.*

The addition of a functional group to a hydrocarbon structure always produces a substance with physical and chemical properties that differ from those of a parent hydrocarbon. The functional group always reacts in a certain way.

Identify *the meaning of each of the following symbols for functional groups.*

* represents   a hydrogen atom, a carbon chain, or a carbon ring

R and R′ represents   any carbon chains or rings bonded to the functional group

Organize *information about organic compounds and their functional groups by completing the table below.*

Compound Type	General Formula	Functional Group
Halocarbon	R-X (X is F, Cl, Br, I)	Halogen
Alcohol	R-OH	Hydroxyl
Ether	R-O-R	Ether
Amine	R-NH2	Amino
Aldehyde	Draw aldehyde here	Carbonyl
Ketone	Draw ketone here	Carbonyl
Carboxylic acid	Draw carboxylic acid here	Carbonyl
Ester	Draw ester here	Ester
Amide	Draw amide here	Amido

Section 22.1 Alkyl Halides and Aryl Halides (continued)

Main Idea	Details

Organic Compounds Containing Halogens

Use with pages 787–788.

Compare and contrast *alkyl halides and aryl halides.*

An alkyl halide is a halocarbon containing a halogen atom covalently bonded to an aliphatic carbon atom. An aryl halide is a halocarbon containing a halogen atom bonded to a benzene ring or other aromatic group.

Naming Halocarbons

Use with page 788.

Describe *how to name halocarbons by completing the following paragraph.*

Organic molecules containing functional groups are given IUPAC names based on their **main-chain alkane structures**. For the alkyl halides, a prefix indicates which **halogen** is present. The prefixes are formed by **changing the -ine at the end of each halogen name to –o**.

Properties and Uses of Halocarbons

Use with page 789.

Examine *Table 22.2 on page 789. Write three observations you make regarding the compounds listed in the table.*
Accept all reasonable responses. Sample answers:

1. As the structure length increases, the boiling point increases.

2. As the structure length increases, the density in liquid state increases.

3. Alkyl halides are named with the halogen and –ane on the end.

Substitution Reactions

Use with page 790.

Sequence *the steps needed to add Cl_2 to ethane to create chloroethane. Use the reaction from the bottom of page 741 in your text as a reference.*

1. Ethane loses a hydrogen.

2. Chlorine gas breaks apart.

3. A chlorine ion is added where the hydrogen was lost on the ethane.

4. The other chlorine bonds with the hydrogen lost from ethane to form HCl.

Create *another substitution reaction using Br2 and methane. Label molecules in each part of the reaction.*

CH_4 + Br_2 → CH_3Br + HBr

Methane + Bromine yields Bromomethane + Hydrobromide

Substituted Hydrocarbons and Their Reactions

Section 22.2 Alcohols, Ethers, and Amines

Main Idea ─── **Details** ──────────────────────

Scan *Section 2 of your text. Use the checklist below as a guide.*

- Read all section titles.
- Read all boldfaced words.
- Read all formulas.
- Look at all figures and read the captions.
- Think about what you already know about alcohols, ethers, and amines.

Write *three facts you discovered about alcohols as you scanned the section.*

1. Accept all reasonable responses.

2. _____

3. _____

New Vocabulary *Use your text to define each term.*

hydroxyl group | an oxygen-hydrogen group covalently bonded to a carbon atom

alcohol | an organic compound in which a hydroxyl group replaces a

hydrogen atom of a hydrocarbon

denatured alcohol | ethanol to which small amounts of noxious materials such as

aviation gasoline have been added to make it unfit to drink

Define the following terms and write the general formula for each term.

ether | an organic compound containing an oxygen atom bonded to two

carbon atoms; general formula: ROR

amine | an organic compound containing nitrogen atoms bonded to carbon

atoms in aliphatic chains or aromatic rings; general formula: RNH_2

Academic Vocabulary *Define the following term.*

bond | to connect, bind, or join

Section 22.2 Alcohols, Ethers, and Amines (continued)

Main Idea —— Details ————————————————————

Alcohols

Use with pages 792–793.

Describe *alcohol by completing the following sentence.*

Because they readily form hydrogen bonds, alcohols have **higher** boiling points and **higher** water solubility than other organic compounds.

Write *the general formula for alcohol:*

ROH

Draw *structures for the following molecules.*

1-butanol

$$H-\underset{\underset{OH}{|}}{\overset{\overset{H}{|}}{C_1}}-\underset{\underset{H}{|}}{\overset{\overset{H}{|}}{C_2}}-\underset{\underset{H}{|}}{\overset{\overset{H}{|}}{C_3}}-\underset{\underset{H}{|}}{\overset{\overset{H}{|}}{C_4}}-H$$

2-butanol

$$H-\underset{\underset{H}{|}}{\overset{\overset{H}{|}}{C_1}}-\underset{\underset{OH}{|}}{\overset{\overset{H}{|}}{C_2}}-\underset{\underset{H}{|}}{\overset{\overset{H}{|}}{C_3}}-\underset{\underset{H}{|}}{\overset{\overset{H}{|}}{C_4}}-H$$

Ethers

Use with page 794.

Describe *ethers by completing the following sentence.*

Ethers are similar to **alcohols** as they are compounds in which oxygen is bonded to **carbon** . Ethers are different from alcohols because the oxygen atom bonds with **two** carbon atoms. Ethers are much less **soluble** in water than alcohol because they have no **hydrogen** to donate to a hydrogen bond.

Section 22.2 Alcohols, Ethers, and Amines (continued)

Main Idea	Details
	Write *the general formula for ethers:*
	ROR´
	Draw *a structure for the following molecule.*
	ethyl ether

$$H-\underset{\underset{H}{|}}{\overset{\overset{H}{|}}{C}}-\underset{\underset{H}{|}}{\overset{\overset{H}{|}}{C}}-O-\underset{\underset{H}{|}}{\overset{\overset{H}{|}}{C}}-\underset{\underset{H}{|}}{\overset{\overset{H}{|}}{C}}-H$$

Amines

Use with page 795

Complete *the following sentence.*

Amines contain __nitrogen__ atoms bonded to carbon atoms in __aliphatic__ chains or __aromatic__ rings. Amines are responsible for many of the __odors__ associated with decay.

Write *the general formula for amines:*

RNH_2

Draw *a structure for the following molecule.*

ethylamine

$$CH_3CH_2$$
$$|$$
$$NH_2$$

Substituted Hydrocarbons and Their Reactions

Section 22.3 Carbonyl Compounds

Main Idea	Details

Skim *Section 3 of your text. Write two questions that come to mind from reading the headings and the illustration captions.*

1. Accept all reasonable responses.

2. _____

New Vocabulary   *Use your text to define each term.*

ketone an organic compound in which the carbon of the carbonyl group is

bonded to two other carbon atoms

carboxylic acid an organic compound that has a carboxyl group

carboxyl group consists of a carbonyl group bonded to a hydroxyl group

ester any organic compound with a carboxyl group in which the hydrogen

of the hydroxyl group has been replaced by an alkyl group

amide an organic compound in which the –OH group of a carboxylic acid is

replaced by a nitrogen atom bonded to other atoms

Define the following terms and write the general formula of each.

carbonyl group functional groups containing an oxygen atom double-bonded to a

carbon atom; general formula: C=O

aldehyde an organic compound in which a carbonyl group located at the end of a carbon

chain bonded to a carbon atom on one side and a hydrogen atom on the other;

general formula: *CHO, where * represents an alkyl group or a hydrogen atom

condensation reaction occurs when two smaller organic molecules combine to form a more

complex molecule, accompanied by the loss of a small molecule;

such as water; general formula: $RCOOH + R'OH \rightarrow RCOOR' + H_2O$

Section 22.3 Carbonyl Compounds (continued)

(**Main Idea**) —————— (**Details**) ——————————————————————

Organic Compounds Containing the Carbonyl Group

Use with pages 796–800.

Identify *five important classes of organic compounds containing or made from carbonyl compounds:*

a. aldehydes _____

b. ketones _____

c. carboxylic acid _____

d. esters _____

e. amides _____

Describe *the common structure of aldehydes and ketones.*

Both have carbonyl functional groups as part of their overall

structure, consisting of an oxygen atom double-bonded to at least

one carbon atom.

Carboxylic Acids

Use with page 798.

Draw *a molecule of a carboxylic acid.*

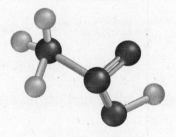

Ethanoic acid
(acetic acid)

Organic Compounds Derived From Carboxylic Acids

Use with pages 799–800.

Describe *organic compounds that are derived from carboxylic acids by completing the following paragraph.*

Several classes of organic compound have structures in which the

___hydrogen or the hydroxyl group___ of a carboxylic acid is replaced

by ___a different atom___ or ___group of atoms___ . The two most com-

mon types are _____esters and amides_____ .

Section 22.3 Carbonyl Compounds (continued)

Main Idea	Details

Condensation Reactions

Use with page 801.

Sequence *the steps for a condensation reaction.*

___3___ A small molecule, such as water, is lost.

___1___ Two organic molecules combine.

___2___ A more complex molecule is formed.

Complete *the following condensation reaction.*

RCOOH + R'OH → _____ **RCOOR' + H₂0** _____

Summarize

Identify *the functional group that corresponds to each of the following:*

a. *-ine* at the end of each halogen name to *–o*   ____halocarbon____

b. adding *–amine* as the suffix   ____amine____

c. *-ane* of the parent alkane to *–ol*   ____alcohol____

d. replacing *–e* ending with *–amide*   ____amide____

e. *–e* at the end of the name to *–al*   ____alkane____

f. *–ane* of the parent alkane to *–anolic acid*   ____carboxylic acid____

g. *-ic acid* ending replaced by *–ate*   ____ester____

h. *–e* end of the alkane replaced by *–one*   ____ketone____

Substituted Hydrocarbons and Their Reactions

Section 22.4 Other Reactions of Organic Compounds

Main Idea	Details

Scan *Section 4 of your text. Use the checklist below as a guide.*

- Read all section titles.
- Read all boldfaced words.
- Read all formulas.
- Look at all figures and read the captions.

Write *three facts you discovered about organic reactions.*

1. Accept all reasonable responses.

2. _____

3. _____

New Vocabulary

Use your text to define each term.

elimination reaction — a reaction in which a combination of atoms is removed from two adjacent carbon atoms, forming an additional bond between the carbon atoms; the eliminated molecules usually form a stable molecule

dehydrogenation reaction — a reaction that eliminates two hydrogen atoms

dehydration reaction — an elimination reaction in which alcohols lose a hydrogen atom and a hydroxyl group to form water

addition reaction — results when other atoms bond to each of two atoms bonded by double or triple covalent bonds

hydration reaction — an addition reaction in which a hydrogen atom and a hydroxyl group from a water molecule add to a double or triple bond

hydrogenation reaction — a reaction that involves the addition of hydrogen to atoms in a double or triple bond

Section 22.4 Other Reactions of Organic Compounds (continued)

Main Idea	Details
Classifying Reactions of Organic Substances *Use with pages 802–805.*	**List** *what needs to happen for chemical reactions of organic substances to occur. Include when and why a catalyst might be needed.*

1. The existing bonds must be broken.

2. New bonds must be formed.

3. Because covalent bonds are strong, many reactions of organic compounds are slow and require continuous input of energy. A catalyst may be needed to speed up reaction.

Review *the section and give an example formula for each of the following reaction types.* **Accept all reasonable responses.**

addition reaction

Alkene + Water → Alcohol

$CH_2=CH_2 + H_2O \rightarrow CH_3-CH_2-OH$

hydration reaction

Alkene + Water → Alcohol

$R - CH = CH_2 + H_2O \rightarrow R-CH_2-CH_2-OH$

dehydrogenation reaction

Ethane → Ethene + Hydrogen

$CH_3-CH_3 \rightarrow CH_2=CH_2 + H_2$

dehydration reaction

Alcohol → Alkene + Water

$R-CH_2-CH_2-OH \rightarrow R-CH=CH_2 + H_2O$

hydrogenation reaction

Alkene + Hydrogen → Alkane

$R-CH=CH_2 + H_2 \rightarrow R-CH_2-CH_3$

elimination reaction

Alkyl halide → Alkene + Hydrogen halide

$R-CH_2-CH_2-X \rightarrow R-CH=CH_2 + HX$

Section 22.4 Other Reactions of Organic Compounds (continued)

Main Idea	Details
Oxidation-Reduction Reactions *Use with Pages 806–807*	**Describe** *oxidation-reduction reactions by completing the following statements.* Many _organic_ compounds can be converted to other compounds by _oxidation_ and _reduction_ reactions. _Oxidation_ is the loss of _electrons_. A substance is oxidized when it gains _oxygen_ or loses _hydrogen_. Reduction is the _gain_ of electrons. A substance is reduced when it loses _oxygen_ or gains _hydrogen_.
Predicting Products of Organic Reactions *Use with Pages 807–808.*	**Write** *the generic equation representing an addition reaction between an alkene and an alkyl halide.* $R-CH=CH-R' + HX \rightarrow R-CHX-CH_2-R'$ **Substitute** *the structure for cyclopentene and the formula for hydrogen bromide. From the equation, you can see that:* A _hydrogen atom_ and a _halide atom_ add across the _double bond_ to form an _alkyl halide_. **Draw** *the formula for the likely product.*

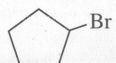

| Cyclopentene | Hydrogen bromide | Bromocyclopentane |

Substituted Hydrocarbons and Their Reactions

Section 22.5 Polymers

Main Idea ———

Details ———————————

Scan *Section 5 of your text. Use the checklist below as a guide.*

• Read all section titles.

• Read all boldfaced words.

• Read all tables and formulas.

• Look at all figures and read the captions.

Write *three facts you discovered about polymers.*

1. Accept all reasonable responses._____

2. _____

3. _____

New Vocabulary *Use your text to define each term.*

polymer | large molecules consisting of many repeating structural units

monomer | a molecule from which a polymer is made

polymerization reaction | a reaction in which monomer units are bonded together to form a polymer

addition polymerization | a reaction in which all of the atoms present in the monomers are

retained in the polymer product

condensation polymerization | a reaction that takes place when monomers containing at least two functional

groups combine with the loss of a small by-product, usually water

thermoplastic | a polymer that can be melted and molded repeatedly into shapes

that are retained when it is cooled

thermosetting | a polymer that can be molded when it is first prepared, but when

cool it cannot be remelted

Section 22.5 Polymers (continued)

Main Idea	Details

The Age of Polymers

Use with page 809.

Identify *three common polymers described in the text. Include their uses.*

1. nonstick cooking surfaces

2. bakelite stove-top appliances

3. compact discs

Reactions Used to Make Polymers

Use with page 810–811.

Identify *the monomers or polymers.*

Monomer (s)	Polymer (s)
Ethylene	**Polyethylene**
Adipic acid and 1, 6 Diamino hexane	Nylon 6.6
Urethane	**Polyurethane**

Compare and contrast *condensation polymerization with addition polymerization by placing the terms below into the Venn diagram.*

- all atoms present in final product
- small by-product, usually water
- involves the bonding of monomers

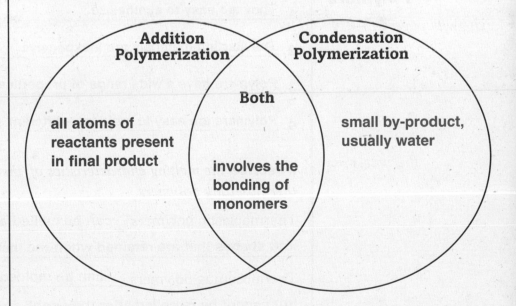

Addition Polymerization — Condensation Polymerization

Both

all atoms of reactants present in final product

involves the bonding of monomers

small by-product, usually water

Section 22.5 Polymers (continued)

Main Idea ————— **Details** —————————————

Common Polymers

Use with page 812.

Identify *the common polymer. Use Table 22.4 in your text as a reference.*

Use	Polymers
Foam furniture cushions	**Polyurethane**
A planter	**Polystyrene**
Nonstick cookware	**Polytetrafluoroethylene (Teflon)**
Food wrap	**Polyethylene or polyvinylidene chloride**
Windows	**Polymethyl methacrylate (Plexiglass)**
Clothing	**Nylon, polyvinyl chloride, polyethylene terephthalate (Dacron or Mylar), polyacrylonitrile (Orlon), or polyvinylidene chloride**
Carpet	**Nylon, polyacrylonitrile (Orlon)**
Water pipes	**Polyvinyl chloride**
Beverage containers	**Polyethylene, polypropylene, polystyrene,or polyethylene terephthalate**

Properties and Recycling of Polymers

Use with pages 813–814.

Identify *four reasons that many different polymers are widely used in manufacturing.*

1. **They are easy to synthesize.**

2. **The starting materials are inexpensive.**

3. **Polymers have a wide range of properties.**

4. **Polymers are easy to mold into different shapes.**

Describe *the melting characteristics of thermoplastic polymers and thermosetting polymers.*

Thermoplastic polymers __**can be melted and molded repeatedly into shapes that are retained when the material cools**__.

Thermosetting polymers __**can be molded when first prepared, but cannot be remelted after they cool**__.

Section 22.5 Polymers (continued)

Main Idea	Details

Discuss *recycling by completing the following paragraph.*

Americans are not efficient at recycling their plastics. Currently, only
_5%_ of plastic waste is recycled. This low rate of _plastics_
recycling is due in part to the _large variety of different plastics_.
Plastics must be _sorted_ according to _polymer composition_,
which is **time-consuming** and _expensive_. The plastic industry has
provided standardized codes that indicate the _composition_ of
each plastic product to make the process easier on individuals.

Describe *what the code of recycling polymers does. Give an example of the code from the textbook.*

The code tells recyclers what types of plastic an object is made from. The

textbook gives the example HDPE with a recycle code of 2. This improves

the process of sorting plastics according to polymer composition.

REAL-WORLD CONNECTION
Describe some common polymers that
you use every day.

Accept all reasonable responses.

_____

_____

_____

_____

Substituted Hydrocarbons and Their Reactions . Chapter Wrap-Up

After reading this chapter, list three things you have learned about substituted hydrocarbons and their reactions.

1. Accept all reasonable responses.

2. _____

3. _____

Review

Use this checklist to help you study.

☐ Study your Science Notebook for this chapter.

☐ Study the definitions of vocabulary words.

☐ Review daily homework assignments.

☐ Reread the chapter and review the tables, graphs, and illustrations.

☐ Review the Section Assessment questions at the end of each section.

☐ Look over the Study Guide at the end of the chapter.

REAL-WORLD CONNECTION

Examine the picture of spooled threads on page 736. Explain how monomers might be a part of the process that produces these spooled polymer threads.

Monomers are individual units which are put together in repeating units to make a polymer.

These synthetic threads are made of repeating units of monomers.

_____

The Chemistry of Life

Before You Read

Review Vocabulary

Define the following terms.

hydrogen bond | a strong dipole-dipole attraction between molecules that contain a hydrogen atom bonded to a small, highly electronegative atom with at least one lone electron pair

isomers | two or more compounds that have the same molecular formula but have different molecular structures

functional group | an atom or group of atoms that always react in a certain way in an organic molecule

polymers | large molecules formed by combining many repeating structural units (monomers); are synthesized through addition or condensation reactions and include polyethylene, polyurethane, and nylon

Chapter 12 | **Illustrate** *the hydrogen bonding between water molecules.*

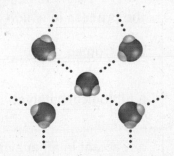

Chapter 22 | **Illustrate** *the molecules for flouroethane and 1,2 difluoropronane.*

```
    H   H
    |   |
H — C — C — F
    |   |
    H   H
  Fluoroethane
```

```
    H   F   H
    |   |   |
H — C — C — C — F
    |   |   |
    H   H   H
  1, 2-Difluoropropane
```

The Chemistry of Life

Section 23.1 Proteins

(Main Idea) ———— **(Details)** ————————————————

Skim *Section 1 of your text. Focus on the headings, subheadings, boldfaced words, and the main ideas. Summarize three main ideas of this section.*

Accept all reasonable responses.

_____

_____

_____

New Vocabulary *Use your text to define each term.*

protein an organic polymer made of amino acids linked together in a specific way

amino acid an organic molecule that has both an amino group and an acidic

carboxyl group

peptide bond the amide bond that joins two amino acids

peptide a chain of two or more amino acids linked together by peptide bonds

denaturation the process in which a protein's natural three-dimensional structure

is disrupted

enzyme a biological catalyst

substrate a reactant in an enzyme-catalyzed reaction

active site the pocket on an enzyme to which the substrate bonds

Section 23.1 Proteins (continued)

Main Idea	Details

Protein Structure

Use with pages 826–829.

Draw *and label a general amino acid with a variable side chain, an amino group, and a carboxyl group.*

R (variable side chain)
|
(amino group) H₂N—C—C—OH (carboxyl group)
| ‖
H   O

Describe *the structure of a dipeptide and its functional units.*

(variable side chain 1)
H   R₁   H R₂ (variable side chain 2)
\ | | |
(amino group) N—C—C—N—C—C—OH (carboxyl group)
/   ‖ | ‖
H   H O H O

Rewrite *each of the following statements, making each true.*

To function properly, each protein must be flat.

To function properly, each protein must be folded into a specific _____

three-dimensional structure. _____

A dipeptide consists of an amino acid with two side chains.

A dipeptide consists of two amino acids bonded together by a _____

peptide bond. _____

Complete *the following paragraph statements about peptide bonds.*

When a peptide bond is formed, **water** is released in the process.

This type of reaction is known as a **condensation** reaction.

Section 23.1 Proteins (continued)

Main Idea ———

Details ——————————————————————

Identify *the peptide bond between the following amino acids.*

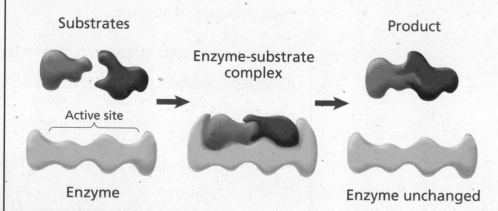

Explain *why Gly-Phe is a different molecule than the Phe-Gly.*

Gly-Phe has a glycine with a free amino group, while Phe-Gly has a

phenylalanine with a free amino group.

Describe *three changes in environment that will uncoil or other-wise denature a protein.*

1. pH_____

2. temperature_____

3. ionic strength_____

The Many Functions of Proteins

Use with pages 829–831.

Draw *an enzyme/substrate complex with the enzyme and substrates labeled.*

Substrates

Active site

Enzyme

Enzyme-substrate complex

Product

Enzyme unchanged

Section 23.1 Proteins (continued)

Main Idea ———— **Details** ————————————————

Describe *how the following functions affect living organisms by giving an example from your text.*

Enzymes: <u>catalyze reactions that go on in living cells, such as</u>

<u>papain which tenderizes meat</u>

Transport proteins: <u>move molecules through body, such as</u>

<u>hemoglobin which carries oxygen in the blood</u>

Structural proteins: <u>form structures vital to organisms, such as</u>

<u>collagen which is part of skin, ligaments, tendons, and bone</u>

Hormones: <u>carry signals from one part of the body to another, such</u>

<u>as insulin which signals body cells that blood sugar is abundant and</u>

<u>should be stored</u>

Review *the statements below and revise to make them correct.*

1. Substrates bind to an enzyme site.

   <u>Substrates bind to an active site.</u>

2. An active site changes shape a great deal to accommodate the substrate.

   <u>An active site changes shape slightly to fit more tightly around</u>

   <u>the substrate.</u>

3. An enzyme-substrate complex changes the enzyme, and it becomes part of the new molecule.

   <u>An enzyme-substrate complex does not change the enzyme, and</u>

   <u>it will not become part of the new molecule.</u>

The Chemistry of Life

Section 23.2 Carbohydrates

Main Idea ——— **Details** ———————————————————

Scan *Section 2 of your text. Use the checklist below as a guide.*

- Read all section titles.
- Read all boldfaced words.
- Look at all figures and read the captions.
- Think about what you already know about carbohydrates.

Write *three facts you discovered about carbohydrates as you scanned the section.*

1. Accept all reasonable responses. _____

2. _____

3. _____

New Vocabulary) *Use your text to define each term.*

carbohydrate compound that contains multiple hydroxyl groups (−OH) as well as

a carbonyl functional group (C=O)

monosaccharide the simplest carbohydrate, often called simple sugar

disaccharide two monosaccharides bonded together

polysaccharide a complex carbohydrate, which is a polymer of simple sugars that

contains 12 or more monomer units

Section 23.2 Carbohydrates (continued)

Main Idea	Details

Kinds of Carbohydrates

Use with pages 832–834.

Draw *the cyclic and open-chain structures of the monosaccharide glucose.*

Cyclic form   Open-chain form

Glucose

Explain *how the monosaccharides glucose and galactose differ. Discuss why they would not react the same way in nature.*

They are stereoisomers. The atoms are bonded in the same order

but are arranged differently in space. A molecule only slightly

different in shape from an enzyme's normal substrate doesn't bond

as well to the active site or undergo the catalyzed reaction.

Describe *the structure and composition of the following types of carbohydrates by completing this table.*

Carbohydrate	Example	Structure and composition
starch	potato	branched or unbranched polymer of glucose
cellulose	lettuce	linear, unbranched polymer of glucose
glycogen	meat	highly branched polymer of glucose
glucose	blood sugar	six-carbon sugar that has an aldehyde structure

The Chemistry of Life

Section 23.3 Lipids

Main Idea ——————— **Details** ——————————————————

Scan *Section 3 of your text. Use the checklist below as a guide.*

• Read all section titles.

• Read all boldfaced words.

• Look at all figures and read the captions.

• Think about what you already know about lipids.

Write *three facts you discovered about lipids as you scanned the section.*

1. Accept all reasonable responses.

2. _____

3. _____

New Vocabulary) *Use your text to define each term.*

lipid | large, nonpolar, biological molecule that is insoluble in water

fatty acid | a long-chain carboxylic acid

triglyceride | three fatty acids bonded to a glycerol backbone through ester bonds

saponification | the hydrolysis of a triglyceride using an aqueous solution of a

strong base to form carboxylate salts and glycerol

phospholipid | a trygliceride in which one of the fatty acids is replaced by a polar

phosphate group

wax | a lipid that is formed by combining a fatty acid with a long-chain alcohol

steroid | a lipid that has multiple cyclic rings in its structure

Section 23.3 Lipids (continued)

Main Idea	Details
What is a lipid? *Use with pages 835–839.*	**Describe** *how a lipid differs from a protein or carbohydrate.* A lipid is unlike proteins and carbohydrates because it is not a polymer with repeating monomer units. **Compare and contrast** *saturated and unsaturated fatty acids. Give an example of each.* Saturated fatty acids contain no double bonds between carbon atoms. Unsaturated fatty acids have one or more double bonds between carbon atoms. An unsaturated fatty acid can become saturated if it reacts with hydrogen. Hydrogenation is an addition reaction in which hydrogen gas reacts with carbon atoms that are linked with multiple bonds. Example: The unsaturated oleic acid can be hydrogenated to form the saturated steric acid. **Explain** *the reactions that form triglycerides. Give the type of reaction as well as the substrates.* Ester bonds in a triglyceride (the product) are formed when the hydroxyl group of glycerol (the substrate) combine with the carboxyl group of a fatty acid (the second substrate).

Section 23.3 Lipids (continued)

(Main Idea)	(Details)

Describe *how waxes are made and what their specific properties include.*

Waxes are formed by combining a fatty acid with a long-chain

alcohol. It is solid at room temperature and is categorized as a fat

with a low melting point.

Describe *a lipid that is not composed of fatty acid chains. Give an example.*

Steroids are lipids that have multiple cyclic rings. Steroids generally

have a four-ring structure. Examples of steroids include cholesterol,

many sex hormones, and vitamin D.

SYNTHESIZE List the important functions for each of the following types of lipids. **Accept all reasonable responses.**

triglyceride stores energy, makes up part of our diet

phospholipid cell membrane component

waxes plants make these to prevent water loss

steroids regulate metabolic processes; a structural component of cell membranes;

vitamin D plays a role in the formation of bones

The Chemistry of Life
Section 23.4 Nucleic Acids

Main Idea	**Details**
	Skim *Section 4 of your text. Write three questions that come to mind from reading the headings and the illustration captions.*
	1. Accept all reasonable responses. Possible answers: What are nucleic acids?
	2. What is the double helix?
	3. What is the difference between DNA and RNA?
New Vocabulary	*Use your text to define each term.*
nucleic acid	a nitrogen-containing biological polymer that is involved in the storage and transmission of genetic information
nucleotide	the monomer that makes up a nucleic acid

Section 23.4 Nucleic Acids (continued)

Main Idea	Details

Structure of Nucleic Acids

Use with page 840.

Draw *a diagram of a nucleotide. Label all of the parts: sugar, phosphate group, and nitrogen-containing base.*

Phosphate group

Sugar

Nitrogen-containing base

Nucleotide

DNA: The Double Helix

Use with pages 841–842.

Write *a statement that differentiates between nucleotides and nucleic acids.*

The monomer that makes up a nucleic acid is called a nucleotide.

Sequence *the events of DNA replication. The first one has been done for you.*

__6__ Hydrogen bonds form between new nitrogen bases and the existing strand.

__2__ Two nucleotide strands unzip.

__5__ Nitrogen bases pair adenine with thymine, cytosine with guanine.

__1__ An enzyme breaks the hydrogen bonds between the nitrogen bases.

__3__ The nucleotide strands separate to expose the nitrogen bases.

__4__ Free nucleotides are delivered by enzymes from the surrounding environment.

Predict *the complimentary base pairing given the following strand of nucleotides.*

A T C T A T C G G A T A T C T G

T A G A T A G C C T A T A G A C

Section 23.4 Nucleic Acids (continued)

Main Idea ———— **Details** ——————————————————————

RNA

Use with page 843.

Identify *differences in DNA and RNA.*

	DNA	RNA
Sugar	deoxyribose	ribose
Nitrogen Bases	A/T/C/G	A/U/C/G
Function	genetic information storage	allows cells to use information found in DNA; protein making
Form of strand	double helix	single strand

State *whether you would find each of the following in DNA, RNA, both, or neither. Explain your answer.*

A-A	neither—don't bind together
A-T	DNA –T only found in DNA
C-G	both C/G found in DNA and RNA
G-A	neither—don't bind together
A-U	RNA – U only found in RNA
U-A	RNA – U only found in RNA

REAL-WORLD CONNECTION

Suppose you are an assistant to a forensic scientist who has found an unknown sample of DNA at a crime scene. Upon analysis, he finds it contains 22% thymine molecules. A DNA sample that contains 40% guanine is obtained from a suspect who is brought in. You ask for the suspect's release. Explain your reasoning based on the bonding patterns of DNA nucleotides.

Because the analysis found 22% T nucleotides, we can assume 22% A nucleotides since they

bond together. This creates 44% of the total nucleotides. The remaining total must be C−G

combinations at 56% (as 44 + 56 = 100%). If the C−G combination is 56% of the total, then the

G must be 1/2 or 28% of the DNA sample. If the suspect brought in has provided a sample that

contains 40% guanine (G), this doesn't match the 28% assumed at the crime scene. The suspect

should be released.

The Chemistry of Life
Section 23.5 Metabolism

Main Idea —————   **Details** ———————————————————

Skim *Section 5 of your text. Focus on the headings, subheadings, boldfaced words, and the main ideas. List three main ideas of this section.*

1. Accept all reasonable responses._____

2. _____

3. _____

New Vocabulary   *Use your text to define each term.*

metabolism	the set of chemical reactions carried out by an organism
catabolism	metabolic reactions that break down complex biological molecules for the purposes of forming smaller building blocks and extracting energy
anabolism	metabolic reactions that use energy and small building blocks to synthesize the complex molecules needed by an organism
ATP	adenosine triphosphate; a nucleotide that functions as the universal energy-storing molecule in living cells
photosynthesis	the process that converts energy from sunlight to chemical energy in the bonds of carbohydrates
cellular respiration	the process in which glucose is broken down to form carbon dioxide, water, and large amounts of energy
fermentation	the process in which glucose is broken down in the absence of oxygen

Academic Vocabulary   *Define the following term.*

conceptualize	visualizing or conceiving an abstract idea in the mind

Section 23.5 Metabolism (continued)

Main Idea	Details

Anabolism and Catabolism

Use with pages 844–845.

Explain *the relationship between metabolism, catabolism, and anabolism.*

Both catabolism and anabolism are metabolic reactions. Catabolism

breaks down complex molecules to extract energy and anabolism

uses energy to make complex molecules.

Explain *how ATP is able to store and release energy in the cells of organisms.*

ATP functions as the universal energy storage molecule in living

cells. During catabolic reactions, the chemical energy from food is

stored in the bonds of ATP. When these bonds are broken, the

chemical energy is released and used during metabolic reactions.

Photosynthesis

Use with page 846.

Write *the reaction of photosynthesis. Label the individual molecules.*

$$6CO_2 + 6H_2O + \text{light energy} \rightarrow C_6H_{12}O_6 + 6O_2$$

Carbon Dioxide   Water   Glucose Oxygen

Identify *the redox process that occurs during photosynthesis.*

The carbon atoms in carbon dioxide are reduced as glucose is

formed. The oxygen atoms in water are oxidized to oxygen gas.

Section 23.5 Metabolism (continued)

Main Idea	Details

Cellular Respiration

Use with page 846.

Write *the reaction of cellular respiration. Be sure to label the individual molecules.*

$$C_6H_{12}O_6 + 6O_2 \rightarrow 6CO_2 + 6H_2O + energy$$

Glucose   Oxygen   Carbon Dioxide   Water

Identify *the redox process that occurs during cellular respiration.*

The carbon atoms in glucose are oxidized to carbon dioxide gas, and

the oxygen atoms in oxygen gas are reduced to the oxygen in water.

_____

Summarize *the relationship between photosynthesis and cellular respiration.*

The products of photosynthesis (glucose and oxygen) are used in cellular

respiration as the substrates. The products of cellular respiration (carbon

dioxide and water) are the substrates needed to start photosynthesis. The

molecules appear in a reversible reaction which either stores or releases

energy. In photosynthesis, the carbon atoms in carbon dioxide are

reduced as glucose is formed, and the oxygen atoms in water are oxidized

to oxygen gas. In cellular respiration, the carbon atoms in glucose are

oxidized to carbon dioxide gas, and the oxygen atoms in oxygen gas are

reduced to the oxygen in water.

_____

Section 23.5 Metabolism (continued)

Main Idea	Details

Fermentation

Use with pages 847–848.

Compare and contrast *alcoholic fermentation and lactic acid fermentation.*

Both alcoholic fermentation and lactic acid fermentation are

anaerobic reactions that metabolize carbohydrates to simple forms

and release energy as ATP. Alcoholic fermentation is a reaction

between yeast and some bacteria to ferment glucose to produce the

alcohol ethanol. Lactic acid formation is a response from muscles

when oxygen is used faster than it can be supplied by the blood.

Through lactic acid fermentation, animal cells produce lactic acid

and a small amount of energy from glucose.

REAL-WORLD CONNECTION Explain why the redox processes that occur during photosynthesis are vital to life.

Accept all reasonable responses. Possible answer: During the redox processes that occur during

photosynthesis, the carbon atoms in carbon dioxide are reduced as glucose is formed and the

oxygen atoms in water are oxidized to oxygen gas. These processes do two things that are vital to

life. First, they return oxygen to the air. All living things need oxygen to provide energy for cells.

Second, they remove carbon dioxide from the air. Since carbon dioxide in high concentrations is

toxic to living things, removing carbon dioxide from air is vital to life.

The Chemistry of Life Chapter Wrap-Up

Now that you have read the chapter, review what you have learned. Write out the major concepts from the chapter.

Accept all reasonable responses.

_____

_____

_____

_____

Review

Use this checklist to help you study.

☐ Study your Science Notebook for this chapter.

☐ Study the definitions of vocabulary words.

☐ Review daily homework assignments.

☐ Reread the chapter and review the tables, graphs, and illustrations.

☐ Review the Section Assessment questions at the end of each section.

☐ Look over the Study Guide at the end of the chapter.

REAL-WORLD CONNECTION

Explain why someone with a liver disorder might be advised to avoid overexertion.

Lactic acid is formed by muscles when oxygen is used faster than it can be supplied by the

blood. Exercise is a major cause of lactic acid formation. Since the liver converts lactic acid

back into glucose for use by the body, someone with a liver disorder might not be able to

convert enough excess lactic acid to keep the body functioning properly.

_____

Nuclear Chemistry

Before You Read

Define the following terms.

isotopes

atoms of the same element with the same number of protons but a

different number of neutrons

nuclear reaction

a reaction that involves a change in the nucleus of an atom

electron

negatively charged particle that is a part of all matter

Chapter 4

Use your text to review the following concepts which will help you understand this chapter.

List *the three kinds of subatomic particles discussed in Chapter 4.*

1. protons

2. neutrons

3. electrons

Draw and label *a nuclear model of the atom. Use Figure 4.14 as a reference.*

Compare students' drawings to Figure 4.14 on page 114 of the

student edition.

Identify *the primary factor in determining an atom's stability.*

its ratio of neutrons to protons

Nuclear Chemistry
Section 24.1 Nuclear Radiation

Main Idea ———— **Details** ————————————————

Skim Section 1 of your text. Write three questions that come to mind from reading the headings and the illustration captions.

1. Accept all reasonable responses._____

2. _____

3. _____

New Vocabulary) *Use your text to define each term.*

radioisotope   isotope of an atom that has an unstable nucleus
_____

X ray   a form of high-energy electromagnetic radiation
_____

penetrating power   the ability of radiation to pass through matter
_____

Section 24.1 Nuclear Radiation (continued)

Main Idea	Details

Comparison of Chemical and Nuclear Reactions

Use with page 860.

Contrast *chemical and nuclear reactions.*

Chemical Reactions	Nuclear Reactions
bonds are **broken** and formed	nuclei emit **rays and/or particles**
atoms are **unchanged**, though they may be rearranged	**atoms** are converted into atoms of another element
reaction rate **influenced** by pressure, temperature, concentration, and catalyst	reaction rate **not affected** by pressure, temperature, concentration, or catalyst
involve only valence **electrons**	may involve protons, **neutrons, or electrons**
small energy changes	**large** energy changes

The Discovery of Radioactivity

Use with pages 860–861.

Summarize *the discovery of radioactivity. Review the dates on the timeline below. Use your text to fill in the important achievements in radioactive research on those dates.*

1895 Roentgen finds invisible rays are emitted when electrons bombard the surface of certain materials.

1895 Becquerel studies minerals that emit light after being exposed to sunlight (phosphorescence).

1898 The Curies identify two new elements, polonium and radium, based on their radioactivity.

1903 The Curies and Becquerel share the Nobel Prize for Physics.

1911 Marie Curie wins the Nobel Prize for Chemistry.

Section 24.1 Nuclear Radiation (continued)

| Main Idea | Details |

Types of Radiation

Use with pages 861–864.

Identify *the common type of radiation signified by each symbol.*

α _____alpha_____

β _____beta_____

γ _____gamma_____

Differentiate *between each of the subatomic radiation particles mentioned in the chapter.*

Radiation Type	Charge	Mass	Relative Penetrating Power
Alpha	2+	6.64×10^{-24} kg	blocked by paper
Beta	1−	9.11×10^{-28} kg	blocked by metal foil
Gamma	0	0	not completely blocked by concrete or lead

Describe *what happens when a radioactive nucleus emits an alpha particle.*

The product nucleus has an atomic number that is lower by 2 and a

mass number that is lower by 4.

Describe *beta particles by completing the following statements.*

A beta particle is a very fast-moving __electron__ . To represent its

insignificant mass, beta particles have a superscript of __zero__ . A

subscript of −1 denotes the __negative__ charge of beta particles.

Beta particles have greater __penetrating power__ than alpha particles.

Describe *what the subscript and superscript of zero tell you about gamma particles.*

The emission of gamma rays does not change the atomic number or

mass number of a nucleus.

Nuclear Chemistry

Section 24.2 Radioactive Decay

Main Idea ———— **Details** ————————————————————

Scan *Section 2, using the checklist below as a guide.*

• Read all section titles and boldfaced words.

• Study all tables, graphs, and figures.

Write *two facts you discovered about transmutation.*

1. Accept all reasonable responses. _____

2. _____

New Vocabulary *Use your text to define each term.*

transmutation	the production of artificial nuclear reactions
nucleon	a proton or a neutron, especially as part of an atomic nucleus
strong nuclear force	a force that acts only on subatomic particles that are extremely close together
band of stability	area on a graph within which all stable nuclei are found
positron emission	a radioactive decay process that involves the emission of a positron from a nucleus
positron	a particle with the same mass as an electron but with opposite charge
electron capture	a process that occurs when the nucleus of an atom draws in a surrounding electron, usually one from the lowest energy level
radioactive decay series	a series of nuclear reactions that begins with an unstable nucleus and results in the formation of a stable nucleus
half-life	a sample size large enough to sustain a nuclear chain reaction
	nuclear reactors able to produce more fuel than they use
radiochemical dating	the combining of atomic nuclei to create energy
	an alternative term for nuclear fusion

Main Idea ——

Details ——

Nuclear Stability

Use with pages 865–866.

Section 24.2 Radioactive Decay (continued)

Contrast *the properties of isotopes by imagining two eggs as models. One isotope would be created using hard-boiled eggs as building blocks, the other using raw eggs as building blocks. Explain which model would be more stable, and which would be more typical of known isotopes.*

The model with hard boiled eggs would be more stable, because it

would be less likely to crack or break. The model with raw eggs would

be more typical, however, since most known isotopes are not stable.

Summarize *how the strong nuclear force helps to keep protons in a nucleus.*

The strong nuclear force acts on both protons and neutrons that are

extremely close together to overcome electrostatic repulsion.

Describe *the neutron-to-proton (n/p) ratio in nuclear stability.*

The number of protons compared to the number of __neutrons__ in a ratio identifies the nuclear ratio. To some degree, the __stability__ of a nucleus can be correlated with its __neutron-to-proton__ ratio. As atomic number __increases__, more __neutrons__ are needed to balance the __electrostatic repulsion__ forces. Plotting the number of neutrons versus the number of __protons__ for all stable nuclei illustrates the __band of stability__.

Types of Radioactive Decay

Use with pages 866–868.

Analyze *the relative stability of radioisotopes. Use Figure 25.8 as a guide.*

1. a radioisotope with too many neutrons relative to its protons
   __above the band of stability__

2. a radioactive isotope __outside the band of stability__

3. a nucleus with more than 83 protons __outside the band of stability__

4. a nucleus with a high atomic number and a neutron-to-proton ratio of 1:5:1. __within the band of stability__

Name_____ Date_____

Section 24.2 Radioactive Decay (continued)

<table>
<tr><td>Main Idea</td><td>Details</td></tr>
<tr><td>

Writing and Balancing Nuclear Equations

Use with page 869.

</td><td>

Compare *positron emission with electron capture.*

Positron emission is __radioactive decay__ that involves the emission of a __positron__ (particle with the same mass as an electron but opposite charge) from a nucleus. During this process, a __proton__ in the nucleus is converted into a neutron and a positron, and then the __positron__ is emitted.

Electron capture is __radioactive decay__ that decreases the number of __protons__ in unstable nuclei lying below the __band of stability__. This occurs when the nucleus of an atom draws in a surrounding __electron__, usually from the lowest energy level. The captured electron combines with a __proton__ to form a __neutron__.

Contrast *balanced chemical equations with balanced nuclear equations.*

Balanced chemical equations conserve __numbers and kinds of atoms__.

Balanced nuclear equations conserve __mass numbers and atomic numbers__.

</td></tr>
<tr><td>

Balancing a Nuclear Equation

Use with Example Problem 24.1, page 869.

</td><td>

Solve *Read Example Problem 24.1 in your text.*

You Try It Problem

Write a balanced nuclear equation for the alpha decay of uranium-238 ($^{238}_{92}$U).

1. **Analyze the Problem**

   Known: reactant: [$^{238}_{92}$U]

   decay type: alpha particle emission ($^{4}_{2}$He)

   Unknown: reaction product $X =$

   balanced nuclear equation =

</td></tr>
</table>

Nuclear Chemistry   343

Section 24.2 Radioactive Decay (continued)

Main Idea ——— **Details** ————————————————————

2. **Solve for the Unknown**

   Using each particle's mass number, make sure the mass number is conserved on each side of the reaction arrow.

   Mass number: $238 = X +$ __4__ $X = 238 - 4$

   Mass number of $X =$ __234__

   Using each particle's atomic number, make sure the atomic number is conserved on each side of the reaction arrow.

   Atomic number: $92 =$ __$X + 2$__ $X = 92 -$ __2__

   Atomic number of $X =$ __90__

   Use the periodic table to identify the unknown element.

   __Thorium-234__

   Write the balanced nuclear equation.

   __$^{238}_{92}U \rightarrow {}^{234}_{90}Th + {}^{4}_{2}He$__

Radioactive Series

Use with page 870.

Describe *a radioactive decay series by completing the following paragraph.*

A radioactive decay series is a series of __nuclear reactions__ that begins with a(n) __unstable__ nucleus and ends in the formation of a stable __nucleus__ . Both alpha decay and __beta decay__ are involved in the process.

Section 24.2 Radioactive Decay (continued)

<table>
<tr>
<td>Main Idea</td>
<td>Details</td>
</tr>
<tr>
<td valign="top">

Radioactive Decay Rates

Use with pages 870–871.

</td>
<td valign="top">

Describe *how Ernest Rutherford's early experiments in inducing nuclear reactions led to modern particle accelerators.*

Rutherford discovered that particles must move at extremely <u>high</u> <u>speeds</u> to overcome electrostatic <u>repulsion</u> and affect a target nucleus. Scientists have built on this to develop methods to accelerate particles to extreme speed using <u>electrostatic</u> and <u>magnetic</u> fields. Particle accelerators use conventional and <u>superconducting</u> magnets to force particles to move at high speeds.

Explain *why some naturally occurring radioactive substances still remain on Earth.*

<u>They have extremely long half-lives.</u>

</td>
</tr>
</table>

REAL-WORLD CONNECTION Suppose you want to join an after-school club. Two clubs interest you. In the photography club, there are a lot of members, but only a few who are truly interested (or proactive) about the topic. Most members just seem to have joined to be involved in an activity (or are neutral). The chemistry club, on the other hand, has fewer members, but there seems to be an equal number of truly interested (proactive) students as there are students without a lot of interest (neutrals). If human interactions followed the same laws as radioisotopes, explain which group would be more stable over the school year.

<u>Answers may vary. Possible answers should include recognition that radioisotopes with</u>

<u>higher numbers of particles and fewer protons tend to be unstable, where radioisotopes</u>

<u>with fewer particles and a balance of protons and neutrons tend to be stable. Using the</u>

<u>parallel with the after-school clubs, the chemistry club would be more stable.</u>

Section 24.2 Radioactive Decay (continued)

(Main Idea) —	(Details)

Calculating the Amount of Remaining Isotope

Use with Example Problem 24.2, page 872.

Solve *Read Example Problem 24.2 in your text.*

You Try It

Problem --------------------------------

Determine the amount of an original sample of 2.0 grams of thorium-234 after 49 days. The half-life of thorium-234 is 24.5 days.

1. Analyze the Problem

Known: Unknown:

Initial amount = __2.0 grams__   Amount remaining = ? g

Elapsed time (t) = ___49___

Half-life (T) = ___24.5___

2. Solve for the Unknown

Number of half-lives (n) = Elapsed time/Half-life

n = 49/24.5 = __2.0 half-lives__

Amount remaining = __(Initial amount)(1/2)^n__

Amount remaining = __(2.0 g)(1/2)$^{2.0}$__

Amount remaining = __2.0 g(1/4)__

Amount remaining = __0.50 g__

3. Evaluate the Answer

After 49 days, __2__ half-lives of thorium-234 have elapsed. The number of half-lives is equivalent to (1/2)(1/2) or __1/4__. The answer, __0.50 g__ is equal to __1/4__ the original quantity.

Radiochemical Dating

Use with pages 873–874.

Write *the balanced nuclear equation for carbon dating.*

$^{14}_{6}C \rightarrow ^{14}_{7}N + \beta$

Nuclear Chemistry
Section 24.3 Nuclear Reactions

Main Idea —— **Details** ————————————————————

Skim *Section 3 of your text. Write three questions that come to mind from reading the headings and the illustration captions. Accept all reasonable responses. Possible answers:*

1. What is induced transmutation?

2. How do nuclear fission and fusion compare and contrast?

3. Why do lighter nuclei tend to undergo fusion?

New Vocabulary) *Use your text to define each term.*

induced transmutation   elements following uranium in the periodic table with atomic

transuranium elements   numbers 93 and greater

the difference in mass between a nucleus and its component nucleons

the splitting of a nucleus into fragments to release energy

mass defect   the difference in mass between a nucleus and its component nucleons

nuclear fission   the splitting of a nucleus into fragments to release energy

critical mass   a sample size large enough to sustain a nuclear chain reaction

breeder reactor   nuclear reactors able to produce more fuel than they use

nuclear fusion   the combining of atomic nuclei to create energy

thermonuclear reaction   an alternative term for nuclear fusion

Academic Vocabulary) *Define the following term.*

generate   to bring into existence

Section 24.3 **Nuclear Reactions** (continued)

⟨**Main Idea**⟩————   ⟨**Details**⟩————————————————

Induced Transmutation

Use with pages 875–876.

Sequence the steps in Rutherford's induced transformation of nitrogen-14 into oxygen.

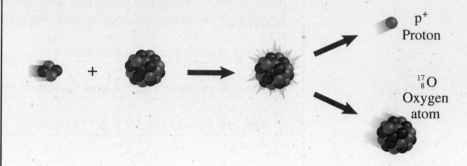

$^4_2$ He bombarding alpha particle
+
[$^{14}_7$ N target nitrogen atom]
→
[$^{18}_9$F unstable fluorine atom]
→
[$^{17}_8$O oxygen atom]
and →
p+ proton

Section 24.3 Nuclear Reactions (continued)

Main Idea	Details

Nuclear Reactions and Energy

Use with pages 877–878.

Write *Einstein's equation. Be sure to include the measurement units.*

$\Delta E = \Delta mc^2$

Identify *the three things you need to know to calculate mass defects.*

a. the mass of a proton

b. the mass of a neutron

c. the mass of the nucleus

Nuclear Fission

Use with pages 878–880.

Organize *the steps in a nuclear fission reaction involving uranium.*

1. A neutron strikes a uranium atom.

2. The uranium transmutates into an unstable nucleus.

3. The nucleus breaks into product isotopes and neutrons,

releasing energy in the process.

Explain *why a fissionable material must have sufficient mass before a sustained reaction can take place.*

Without sufficient mass, neutrons escape before they strike other

nuclei and continue the chain reaction.

Explain *why a fissionable material must not have an excess of mass.*

With an excess of mass, the reaction rapidly escalates, leading to a

violent nuclear explosion.

Section 24.3 Nuclear Reactions (continued)

Main Idea —— **Details** ————————————————

Nuclear Reactors

Use with pages 880–882.

Describe *how a nuclear reactor creates energy. Include how the environment is protected from nuclear waste.*

Nuclear fission produces __energy generated by nuclear reactors__.

A common fuel is __fissionable uranium (IV) oxide encased__

__in corrosion-resistant fuel rods__. A neutron-emitting source

__starts the reaction__ and control rods absorb virtually all of the

__neutrons__ produced in the reaction. Heat from a reaction is used

to power __steam-driven turbines__ which produce electrical power.

Nuclear Fusion

Use with pages 883–884.

Describe *nuclear fusion by completing the following paragraph.*

Nuclear fusion is the combining of atomic __nuclei__. Nuclear fusion

reactions are capable of __releasing very large amounts of energy__.

The most common fusion reaction is the __Sun__. Because of the

energy requirements, fusion reactions are also known as

__thermonuclear reactions__.

Explain *why fusion reaction is not yet a practical source of every-day energy.*

__Very high temperatures are required to produce nuclear fusion__

__reactions. In addition, they are difficult to contain because of the__

__high amounts of energy released. There are currently no materials__

__capable of withstanding the high temperatures required for a fusion__

__reaction.__

REAL-WORLD CONNECTION

Create a metaphor from everyday life that will show the difference between nuclear fission and nuclear fusion.

Accept all reasonable responses. Possible answers:

Nuclear fusion requires __combining nuclei to form a more stable nucleus.__

Nuclear fusion requires __breaking down an atom to release energy.__

Fusion is like: __getting people with different opinions to come to a consensus.__

Fusion is like: __a club formed by people with common interests that breaks up into__

__smaller clubs because its members can't agree on what activities to do.__

Nuclear Chemistry

Section 24.4 Applications and Effects of Nuclear Reactions

Main Idea	**Details**
	Scan *Section 4, using the checklist below as a guide.*
	• Read all section titles.
	• Read all boldfaced words.
	• Read all tables and graphs.
	• Look at all pictures and read the captions.
	• Think about what you already know about radioactive decay.
	Write *three questions you have about nuclear radiation.*
	Accept all reasonable responses. Possible answers:
	1. What is ionizing radiation?
	2. How does radiation affect my body?
	3. What are the effects of radiation exposure?
New Vocabulary	*Use your text to define each term.*
ionizing radiation	radiation energetic enough to ionize matter with which it collides
radiotracer	a radioisotope that emits non-ionizing radiation and is used to signal the presence of an element or specific substance

Section 24.4 Applications and Effects of Nuclear Reactions (continued)

Main Idea	Details
Detecting Radioactivity Use with pages 885–886.	**List** *and describe three methods of detecting radiation.* 1. Film badges contain radiation-sensitive film used to monitor radiation exposure. 2. Geiger counters measure the amount of ionizing radiation present. 3. Scintillation counters produce bright flashes of light when ionizing radiation is present.
Uses of Radiation Use with pages 886–888.	**Describe** *how a radiotracer works.* A radiotracer is a **radioisotope** that emits **non-ionizing radiation** and is used to signal the presence of **an element** or specific substance. The fact that all of an element's isotopes have the same **chemical properties** makes the use of radioisotopes possible. **Discuss** *a common radiotracer that is used in medicine.* Iodine-131 is commonly used to detect **diseases** associated with the **thyroid gland**. A doctor will give the patient a drink containing a small amount of iodine-131. The iodine-containing **radioisotope** is then used to monitor the function of the thyroid gland.

Section 24.4 Applications and Effects of Nuclear Reactions (continued)

Main Idea —————

Details —————————————————————————

Biological Effects of Radiation

Use with pages 888–890.

Identify *three factors that affect the possible damage to the body caused by ionizing radiation discussed in the textbook.*

1. energy of the radiation

2. type of tissue absorbing the radiation

3. distance from the source

Discuss *genetic and somatic damage caused by ionizing radiation.*

Somatic damage affects **only nonreproductive body tissues and** therefore affects the organism only during its lifespan.

Genetic damage can affect **offspring because it damages** reproductive tissue, which may affect genes and chromosomes.

Genetic damage is more difficult to study because the effects may not be seen for several generations.

REAL-WORLD CONNECTION Create a warning label that will identify the dangers of a radioactive material to users.

Accept all reasonable responses. Possible answer: WARNING: Radiation can cause damage to body tissues, including genes and chromosomes in reproductive cells. Individuals should limit their exposure to radiation.

Nuclear Chemistry Chapter Wrap-Up

After reading this chapter, list three important facts you have learned about nuclear chemistry.

1. <u>Accept all reasonable responses.</u>

2. _____

3. _____

Review

Use this checklist to help you study.

☐ Study your Science Notebook for this chapter.

☐ Study the definitions of vocabulary words.

☐ Review daily homework assignments.

☐ Reread the chapter and review the tables, graphs, and illustrations.

☐ Review the Section Assessment questions at the end of each section.

☐ Look over the Study Guide at the end of the chapter.

REAL-WORLD CONNECTION

Imagine you are watching a program on radiation with a friend. Your friend is afraid of all radiation. Explain to your friend some of the common useful applications of radiation.

<u>While there are many reasons to be concerned about radiation, there are some common</u>

<u>useful applications. Radiotracers which emit non-ionizing radiation are used to diagnose</u>

<u>disease and to analyze complex chemical reaction mechanisms. Nuclear reactors generate</u>

<u>steam, which is used to produce electrical power.</u>